WELCOME

TO YOUR NEW CHICKEN SOUP FOR THE SOUL® PERSONAL ORGANIZER

The Chicken Soup for the Soul® family of authors and publishers are excited to bring you this specially designed inspirational organizer. It is our hope that this tool will help bring balance and organization to your busy life. Before starting, please take a few moments to review the enclosed user guide. This will help you get the most out of your new organizer. Good luck and enjoy!

"Organize with inspiration from the Soul"

If there is light in the soul,
There will be beauty in the person.
If there is beauty in the person,
There will be harmony in the house.
If there is harmony in the house.
There will be order in the nation.
If there is order in the nation.
There will be peace in the world.
Chinese Proverb

Personal Information

MY DATA

NAME Erin Pang

ADDRESS 546 Altamont Dr

Milpitas, CA 95035

TEL: (408) 946-2381 FAX: ( )

DRIVER'S LIC.#

LAWYER ( )

ACCOUNTANT ( )

OTHER ( )

HEALTH / MEDICAL WHO TO NOTIFY IN AN EMERGENCY

NAME

ADDRESS

HEALTH CARD #

CLOSEST HOSPITAL ( )

OTHER HEALTH CLINIC ( )

DOCTOR (FAMILY) Dr. Gloria Wang ( )

DOCTOR (EYE) Dr. Somi Oh ( )

DOCTOR (OTHER) ( )

DENTIST (FAMILY) Galen Wong ( )

INSURANCE (COMPANY / NAME)

HOME ( )

AUTO ( )

LIFE ( )

OTHER ( )

Chicken Soup for the Soul® - Date-Your-Own, Wire-Bound

Canadian Cataloging in Publication Data, National Library of Canada

ISBN 1-894316-00-2

Publisher: Inspirational Planners Incorporated, 53 Queen's Plate Drive, Unit 4, Etobicoke, Ontario, Canada M9W 6P1
1-800-851-8540 USA/Canada

Manufacturer: Day-Timers, Inc., One Willow Lane, East Texas, PA 18046 • 1-800-277-3642 (USA) or 1-800-387-4168 (Canad

MONTH OF September

THE MIRACLE BRIDGE

The Brooklyn Bridge that spans the river between Manhattan and Brooklyn is simply an engineering miracle. In 1883, a creative engineer, John Roebling, was inspired by an idea for this spectacular bridge project. However, bridge-building experts told him to forget it, it just was not possible. Roebling convinced his son, Washington, an up-and-coming engineer, that the bridge could be built. The two of them conceived the concept of how it could be accomplished and how to overcome the obstacles. Somehow they convinced bankers to finance the project. Then, with unharnessed excitement and energy, they hired their crew and began to build their dream bridge.

The project was only a few months under way when a tragic on-site accident killed John Roebling and severely injured his son. Washington was severely brain-damaged, unable to talk or walk. Everyone thought the project would have to be scrapped, since the Roeblings were the only ones who understood how the bridge could be built.

Though Washington Roebling was unable to move or talk, his mind was as sharp as ever. One day as he lay in his hospital bed, an idea flashed in his mind as to how to develop a communication code. All he could move was one finger, so he touched the arm of his wife with that finger. He tapped out the code to communicate to her what she was to tell the engineers who continued building the bridge. For 13 years, Washington tapped out his instructions with one finger until the spectacular Brooklyn Bridge was finally completed.

A Fresh Packet of Sower's Seeds

THINGS TO DO	Sunday	Monday	Tuesday
	28	29	30
	4	5	6
	NOTES		

Note special events to secure their memory

Month September 2005

Wednesday	Thursday	Friday	Saturday
31	Sept 1	2	3

NOTES

Chicken Soup for the Soul ®

CONSIDER THIS

In 1935, the New York Herald Tribune's review of George Gershwin's classic Porgy and Bess stated that it was "Sure-fire rubbish."

Jack Canfield & Mark Victor Hansen

Notes & Tasks

Take note of the little things...
you will learn that details do count.

Date ______________________

✓

Remember *Dry Cleaning ... Movie Rentals ... Reservations ... Special Events ... and a whole lot more!*

MONTH OF ____________

THE PRETTIEST ANGEL

For the past 20 years I have spoken to all kinds of audiences in the character of Benjamin Franklin. Even though the majority of my engagements are before corporate and conventional audiences, I still like to talk to school groups. When I work for corporate clients outside the Philadelphia area, I ask them to sponsor appearances in two schools as a service to their community.

I find that even very young children relate well to the message I present even through the character of Benjamin Franklin. I always encourage them to ask any questions they wish, so I usually get some interesting ones. The character of Benjamin Franklin often becomes so real to these students that they willingly suspend disbelief and are caught up in a dialogue with me as if I am really Ben Franklin.

On one particular day after an assembly for an elementary school, I was visiting a fifth-grade classroom to answer questions for students who were studying American history. One student raised his hand and said, "I thought you died." This was not an unusual question and I answered it by saying, "Well, I did die on April 17, 1790, when I was 84 years old, but I didn't like it and I'm never going to do it again."

I immediately asked for any other questions and called on a boy at the back of the room who raised his hand. He asked, "When you were in Heaven, did you see my mother there?"

My heart stopped. I wanted the floor to open up and swallow me. My only thought was, "Don't blow this!" I realized for an 11-year-old boy to ask that question in front of all his classmates it had to either be a very recent occurrence or of utmost concern. I also knew I had to say something.

Then I heard my voice say: "I'm not sure if she is the one I think she was, but if she is, she was the prettiest angel there."

The smile on his face told me that it was the right answer. I'm not sure where it came from, but I think I just may have had a little help from the prettiest angel there.

Ralph Archbold

THINGS TO DO

Sunday

Monday

Tuesday

NOTES

Note special events to secure their memory

Month

Wednesday	Thursday	Friday	Saturday

NOTES

Chicken Soup for the Soul®

CONSIDER THIS

Beethoven handled the violin awkwardly and preferred playing his own compositions instead of improving his technique. His teacher called him hopeless as a composer.

Jack Canfield & Mark Victor Hansen

Notes & Tasks

Take note of the little things...
you will learn that details do count.

Date ______________________

		✓

Remember
Dry Cleaning ... Movie Rentals ... Reservations ... Special Events ... and a whole lot more!

MONTH OF ____________________

CHILDREN LEARN WHAT THEY LIVE

If children live with criticism,
they learn to condemn.
If children live with hostility,
they learn to fight.
If children live with fear,
they learn to be apprehensive.
If children live with pity,
they learn to feel sorry for themselves.
If children live with ridicule,
they learn to be shy.
If children live with jealousy,
they learn what envy is.
If children live with shame,
they learn to feel guilty.
If children live with tolerance,
they learn to be patient.
If children live with encouragement,
they learn to be confident.
If children live with praise,
they learn to appreciate.
If children live with approval,
they learn to like themselves.
If children live with acceptance,
they learn to find love in the world
If children live with recognition,
they learn to have a goal.
If children live with sharing,
they learn to be generous.
If children live with honesty and fairness,
they learn what truth and justice are.
If children live with security,
they learn to have faith in themselves
and in those around them.
If children live with friendliness,
they learn that the world is a nice
place in which to live.
If children live with serenity,
they learn to have peace of mind.
With what are your children living?

Dorothy Law Nolte has taught family life education for over 35 years. She wrote Children Learn What They Live for her newspaper column, Creative Family Living. There are many truncated versions. The poem as you see it printed above is the complete version used by her students. CLWTL has been translated into fifteen languages and is used by parents and educators throughout the world. Look for the book, Children Learn What They Live - Parenting to Inspire Values by Dorothy L. Nolte and Rachel Harris, Workman Publishing 1998.

THINGS TO DO

Sunday | Monday | Tuesday

NOTES

Note special events to secure their memory

Month

Wednesday	Thursday	Friday	Saturday

NOTES

Chicken Soup for the Soul ®

CONSIDER THIS

Thomas Edison's teacher said he was too stupid to learn anything.

Jack Canfield & Mark Victor Hansen

Notes & Tasks

Take note of the little things...
you will learn that details do count.

Date ______________________

		✓

Remember *Dry Cleaning ... Movie Rentals ... Reservations ... Special Events ... and a whole lot more!*

MONTH OF ____________

FIVE MINUTES ON MONDAY MORNING

As we move through time, our lives become intertwined with the lives of others–a weaving, in and out–the minutes and hours becoming the threads that bind us all together. As the turns and twists of our lives touch the lives of others, there are people who make a difference to the direction we may take. They are those who provide us with a gift–maybe a gift of guidance or understanding–sometimes the gift is only a few precious moments they have shared with us, to let us know that they care.

Weave into your life a time for yourself–a time to remember those people who have helped shape you, and the destiny you are unfolding. Set aside a few minutes each week, put it into your planner.

Monday morning works best for me. I stay in bed for five extra minutes awake, with my eyes closed. I think about someone either in my past or present, and bring their face to mind. There, in the safety and warmth of my bed, I thank that person for the gift they brought into my life–a simple kindness from a childhood friend, or a great laugh I may have recently shared with a coworker. If possible, before I go to work I call and tell the person how grateful I am that they have shared my life. Plan to tell at least one person a week what a difference they have made. There is no better way to start a week!

Patty Hansen

THINGS TO DO

Sunday	Monday	Tuesday

NOTES

Note special events to secure their memory

Month

Wednesday	Thursday	Friday	Saturday

NOTES

Chicken Soup for the Soul ®

CONSIDER THIS

When Lucy Ball began studying to be an actress in 1927, she was told by the head instructor of the John Murray Anderson Drama School, "Try any other profession. Any other."

Jack Canfield & Mark Victor Hansen

Notes & Tasks

Take note of the little things...
you will learn that details do count.

Date ______________________

✓

Remember
Dry Cleaning ... Movie Rentals ... Reservations ... Special Events ... and a whole lot more!

MONTH OF ____________________

THE RULES FOR BEING HUMAN

1. **You will receive a body.**
   You may like it or hate it, but it will be yours for the entire period of this time around.
2. **You will learn lessons.**
   You are enrolled in a full-time informal school called Life. Each day in this school you will have the opportunity to learn lessons. You may like the lessons or think them irrelevant and stupid.
3. **There are no mistakes, only lessons.**
   Growth is a process of trial and error: Experimentation. The "failed" experiments are as much a part of the process as the experiment that ultimately "works."
4. **A lesson is repeated until learned.**
   A lesson will be presented to you in various forms until you have learned it. When you have learned it, you can then go on to the next lesson.
5. **Learning lessons does not end.**
   There is no part of life that does not contain its lessons. If you are alive, there are lessons to be learned.
6. **"There" is no better than "here."**
   When your "there" has become a "here," you will simply obtain another "there" that will again look better than "here."
7. **Others are merely mirrors of you.**
   You cannot love or hate something about another person unless it reflects something you love or hate about yourself.
8. **What you make of your life is up to you.**
   You have all the tools and resources you need.
   What you do with them is up to you. The choice is yours.
9. **Your answers lie inside you.**
   The answers to Life's questions lie inside you.
   All you need to do is look, listen and trust.
10. **You will forget all this.**

Chérie Carter-Scott

THINGS TO DO

Sunday	Monday	Tuesday

NOTES

Note special events to secure their memory

Month

Wednesday	Thursday	Friday	Saturday

NOTES

Chicken Soup for the Soul®

CONSIDER THIS

In 1959, a Universal Pictures executive dismissed Clint Eastwood and Burt Reynolds at the same meeting with the following statements. To Burt Reynolds: "You have no talent." To Clint Eastwood: "You have a chip on your tooth, your Adam's apple sticks out to far and you talk too slow."

Jack Canfield & Mark Victor Hansen

Notes & Tasks

Take note of the little things...
you will learn that details do count.

Date ______________________

✓

Remember *Dry Cleaning ... Movie Rentals ... Reservations ... Special Events ... and a whole lot more!*

MONTH OF ____________________

MIKEY'S GOAL

Last night was the last game for my eight-year-old son's soccer team. It was the final quarter. The score was two to one, my son's team in the lead. Parents encircled the field, offering encouragement. With less then 10 seconds remaining, the ball rolled in front of my son's teammate, one Mikey O'Donnel. With shouts of "Kick it!" echoing across the field, Mikey reared back and gave it everything he had. All around me the crowd erupted. O'Donnel had scored!

Then there was silence. Mikey had scored all right, but in the wrong goal, ending the game in a tie. For a moment there was total hush. You see, Mikey has Down's syndrome and for him there is no such thing as a wrong goal. All goals were celebrated by a joyous hug from Mikey. He had even been known to hug the opposing players when they scored.

The silence was finally broken when Mikey, his face filled with joy, grabbed my son, hugged him and yelled, "I scored! I scored. Everybody won! Everybody won!" For a moment I held my breath, not sure how my son would react. I need not have worried. I watched, through tears, as my son threw up his hand in the classic high-five salute and started chanting, "Way to go Mikey! Way to go Mikey!" Within moments both teams surrounded Mikey, joining in the chant and congratulating him on his goal. Later that night, when my daughter asked who had won, I smiled as I replied, "It was a tie. Everybody won."

Kim Kane

THINGS TO DO

Sunday

Monday

Tuesday

NOTES

Note special events to secure their memory

Month

Wednesday	Thursday	Friday	Saturday

NOTES

Chicken Soup for the Soul ®

CONSIDER THIS

In 1962, four nervous young musicians played for the executives of the Decca Recording Company. The executives were not impressed. While turning down this British rock group called the Beatles, one executive said, "We don't like their sound. Groups of guitars are on the way out."

Jack Canfield & Mark Victor Hansen

Notes & Tasks

*Take note of the little things...
you will learn that details do count.*

Date ____________________

		✓

Remember *Dry Cleaning ... Movie Rentals ... Reservations ... Special Events ... and a whole lot more!*

MONTH OF ____________________

REMEMBER, WE'RE RAISING CHILDREN, NOT FLOWERS!

I was buying a sport coat a few weeks ago and Mark Michaels, the owner of the store, and I were discussing parenting. He told me that while he and his wife and seven-year-old daughter were out for dinner, his daughter knocked over her water glass. After the water was cleaned up without any recriminating remarks from her parents, she looked up and said, "You know, I really want to thank you guys for not being like other parents. Most of my friends' parents would have yelled at them and given them a lecture about paying more attention. Thanks for not doing that!"

Once, when I was having dinner with some friends, a similar incident happened. Their five-year-old son knocked over a glass of milk at the dinner table. When they immediately started in on him, I intentionally knocked my glass of milk over, too. When I started to explain how I still knock things over even at the age of 48, the boy started to beam and the parents seemingly got the message and backed off. How easy it is to forget that we are all still learning.

Jack Canfield

THINGS TO DO

Sunday

Monday

Tuesday

NOTES

Note special events to secure their memory

Month

Wednesday	Thursday	Friday	Saturday

NOTES

Chicken Soup for the Soul ®

CONSIDER THIS

When Alexander Graham Bell invented the telephone in 1876, it did not ring off the hook with calls from potential backers. After making a demonstration call, President Rutherford Hayes said, "That's an amazing invention, but who would ever want to use one of them?"

Jack Canfield & Mark Victor Hansen

Notes & Tasks

*Take note of the little things...
you will learn that details do count.*

Date ______________________

✓

Remember Dry Cleaning ... Movie Rentals ... Reservations ... Special Events ... and a whole lot more!

MONTH OF ______________________

DINNER OUT

As my bride of many years greeted me one evening, her voice blasted through the door, "Guess what?"

I always take a deep breath on this very leading question. "What?" I asked.

"I just won a sales contest at work and the prize is dinner for two at the new fancy restaurant down by the riverfront!"

Her excitement was contagious. We knew the restaurant was posh because we could only understand parts of the menu. "See? I told you there would be a place for me to wear my new spring outfit," she coyly reminded me.

"Two can play at that game," I responded. "I will wear my gray, my Borsalino imported straw hat and a new silk tie. We will be dressed to the nines. This town will never be the same. Almost like our first date."

It was early spring and nearing dusk as the maître d' escorted us to a table by a window, with a view of the river. And the table was beautifully set, with a smoke-gray tablecloth accented by bright red napkins, lemon slices in the long-stemmed water glasses, fresh flowers--the works.

We reminisced about our children and grandchildren and their impact on our lives. A delicious meal savored in such an atmosphere should be remembered a long time. As it turned out, this will probably never be forgotten.

As the shadows lengthened, the riverboats rocking in their berths, I murmured, "Why don't we sashay down the esplanade like we did in Paris a few years ago? Remember the fun we had?"

Hand in hand, we strolled by the stores. People smiled and nodded. Lots of smiling and nodding, in fact. "I never realized there were so many friendly people as we have seen this evening, dear," I observed.

"Probably your new straw hat. Or the fact that you're such a handsome devil," she countered.

We completed the walking tour past the store windows. After acknowledging many smiles, we found ourselves back at the restaurant, looking at our reflection in the window. It was then that I saw the reason for all the smiles.

Caught in the fly of my trousers and hanging down for all to see was a bright red napkin from the restaurant!

Duke Raymond

THINGS TO DO

Sunday | **Monday** | **Tuesday**

NOTES

Note special events to secure their memory

Month

Wednesday	Thursday	Friday	Saturday

NOTES

Chicken Soup for the Soul ®

CONSIDER THIS

When Pablo Casals reached 95, a young reporter threw him the following question. "Mr. Casals, you are 95 and the greatest cellist that ever lived. Why do you still practice six hours a day?" Mr. Casals answered, "Because I think I'm making progress."

Jack Canfield & Mark Victor Hansen

Notes & Tasks

Take note of the little things...
you will learn that details do count.

Date ______________________

✓

Remember *Dry Cleaning ... Movie Rentals ... Reservations ... Special Events ... and a whole lot more!*

MONTH OF ______________________

RISKING

Two seeds lay side by side in the fertile spring soil.

The first seed said, "I want to grow! I want to send my roots deep into the soil beneath me, and thrust my sprouts through the earth's crust above me... I want to unfurl my tender buds like banners to announce the arrival of spring...I want to feel the warmth of the sun on my face and the blessing of the morning dew on my petals!"

And so she grew.

The second seed said, "I am afraid. If I send my roots into the ground below, I don't know what I will encounter in the dark. If I push my way through the hard soil above me I may damage my delicate sprouts.... what if I let my buds open and a snail tries to eat them? And if I were to open my blossoms, a small child may pull me from the ground. No, it is much better for me to wait until it is safe."

And so she waited.

A yard hen scratching around in the early spring ground for food found the waiting seed and promptly ate it.

MORAL OF THE STORY

Those of us who refuse to risk and
grow get swallowed up by life.

Patty Hansen

THINGS TO DO

Sunday | Monday | Tuesday

NOTES

Note special events to secure their memory

Month

Wednesday	Thursday	Friday	Saturday

NOTES

Chicken Soup for the Soul ®

CONSIDER THIS

After having his cancer-ridden leg amputated, young Canadian Terry Fox vowed to run on one leg from coast to coast the entire length of Canada to raise $1 million for cancer research. Forced to quit halfway the cancer invaded his lungs, he and the foundation he started have raised over $20 million for cancer research.

Jack Canfield & Mark Victor Hansen

Notes & Tasks

Take note of the little things...
you will learn that details do count.

Date ______________________

		✓

Remember *Dry Cleaning ... Movie Rentals ... Reservations ... Special Events ... and a whole lot more!*

MONTH OF ____________________

THE MOST BEAUTIFUL FLOWER

The park bench was deserted as I sat down to read
Beneath the long, straggly branches of an old willow tree.
Disillusioned by life with good reason to frown,
For the world was intent on dragging me down.
And if that weren't enough to ruin my day,
A young boy out of breath approached me, all tired from play.
He stood right before me with his head tilted down
And said with great excitement, "Look what I found!"
In his hand was a flower, and what a pitiful sight,
With its petals all worn-not enough rain, or too little light.
Wanting him to take his dead flower and go off and play,
I faked a small smile and then shifted away.
But instead of retreating he sat next to my side
And placed the flower to his nose and declared with overacted surprise,
"It sure smells pretty and it's beautiful, too.
"That's why I picked it; here, it's for you."
The weed before me was dying or dead.
Not vibrant of colors, orange, yellow or red.
But I knew I must take it, or he might never leave.
So I reached for the flower, and replied, "Just what I need."
But instead of him placing the flower in my hand,
He held it midair without reason or plan.
It was then that I noticed for the very first time
That weed-toting boy could not see: he was blind.
I heard my voice quiver, tears shone like the sun
As I thanked him for picking the very best one.
"You're welcome," he smiled, and then ran off to play,
Unaware of the impact he'd had on my day.
I sat there and wondered how he managed to see
A self-pitying woman beneath an old willow tree.
How did he know of my self-indulged plight?
Perhaps from his heart, he'd been blessed with true sight.
Through the eyes of a blind child, at last I could see
The problem was not with the world; the problem was me.
And for all of those times I myself had been blind,
I vowed to see the beauty in life, and appreciate every second that's mine.
And then I held that wilted flower up to my nose
And breathed in the fragrance of a beautiful rose
And smiled as I watched that young boy, another weed in his hand
About to change the life of an unsuspecting old man.

Cheryl L. Costello-Forshey

THINGS TO DO

Sunday

Monday

Tuesday

NOTES

Note special events to secure their memory

Month

Wednesday	Thursday	Friday	Saturday

NOTES

Chicken Soup for the Soul®

CONSIDER THIS

Sheila Holzworth lost her sight when she was only 10 years old. The orthodontic head gear that was attached to her braces snapped and gouged her eyes. Despite her lack of sight, she went on to become an internationally known athlete whose accomplishments included climbing to the icy summit of Mount Rainier in 1981.

Jack Canfield & Mark Victor Hansen

Notes & Tasks

Take note of the little things...
you will learn that details do count.

Date ______________________

		✓

Remember
Dry Cleaning ... Movie Rentals ... Reservations ... Special Events ... and a whole lot more!

MONTH OF ____________________

TWO NICKELS AND FIVE PENNIES

In the days when an ice cream sundae cost much less, a 10-year-old boy entered a hotel coffee shop and sat at a table. A waitress put a glass of water in front of him. "How much is an ice cream sundae?"

"Fifty cents," replied the waitress.

The little boy pulled his hand out of his pocket and studied a number of coins in it. "How much is a dish of plain ice cream?" he inquired.

Some people were now waiting for a table and the waitress was a bit impatient. "Thirty-five cents," she said brusquely.

The little boy again counted the coins. "I'll have the plain ice cream," he said.

The waitress brought the ice cream, put the bill on the table, and walked away. The boy finished the ice cream, paid the cashier and departed. When the waitress came back, she began wiping down the table and then swallowed hard at what she saw. There, placed neatly beside the empty dish, were two nickels and five pennies -- her tip.

The Best of Bits & Pieces

Character cannot be developed in ease and quiet.
Only through experiences of trial and suffering can the soul
be strengthened, vision cleared, ambition inspired and success achieved.

Helen Keller

THINGS TO DO

Sunday | Monday | Tuesday

NOTES

Note special events to secure their memory

Month

Wednesday	Thursday	Friday	Saturday

NOTES

Chicken Soup for the Soul ®

CONSIDER THIS

During the first year of business, the Coca-Cola Company sold only 400 Cokes.

Jack Canfield & Mark Victor Hansen

Notes & Tasks

*Take note of the little things...
you will learn that details do count.*

Date ______________________

		✓

Remember Dry Cleaning ... Movie Rentals ... Reservations ... Special Events ... and a whole lot more!

MONTH OF ______________________

THE LITTLE RED WAGON

My friend Gayle has been "living" with cancer for four years and it is progressively getting worse. During a conversation with another friend, Gayle expressed that one of her childhood wishes was to have a red Radio Flyer wagon. As a child she never received one because she believed that if you told your birthday wish it wouldn't come true. I was at an ice cream stand one day and in the window was a miniature red Radio Flyer wagon that could be won in a weekly drawing. Every time you made a purchase you could fill out a ticket for a chance to win. After several weeks and many ice cream cones, I didn't win. I got up the courage to ask the person in charge if I could buy one. I went to the window and as I began to tell my story, I could feel my throat tighten and my eyes overflowed with tears. Somehow I managed to explain my reason for wanting to purchase the wagon, and after writing a check, I left carrying it. The wagon was delivered the next day, and for Gayle it was a dream come true. The following day I received a letter that read:

Dear Bonnie,
Every once in a while there is an opportunity to pass on a kindness--no questions asked. I lost my parents to cancer six months apart from each other. I cared for both of them but could not have done it without the love and generosity of friends--friends who care.
The best to you,
Norma

It was from the owner of the ice cream stand. Enclosed was my uncashed check.

Bonita L. Anticola

THINGS TO DO

Sunday

Monday

Tuesday

NOTES

Note special events to secure their memory

Month

Wednesday	Thursday	Friday	Saturday

NOTES

Chicken Soup for the Soul®

CONSIDER THIS

Playwright Tennessee Williams was enraged when his play "Me Vasha" was not chosen in a class competition at Washington University where he was enrolled in English XVI. The teacher recalled that Williams denounced the judges' choices and their intelligence.

Jack Canfield & Mark Victor Hansen

Notes & Tasks

Take note of the little things...
you will learn that details do count.

Date ______________________

✓

Remember *Dry Cleaning ... Movie Rentals ... Reservations ... Special Events ... and a whole lot more!*

Month

Wednesday	Thursday	Friday	Saturday

NOTES

Chicken Soup for the Soul ®

CONSIDER THIS

George MacDonald once noted that one draft horse can move two tons of weight. However, two draft horses in harness, working together, can move twenty-three tons of weight.

Jack Canfield & Mark Victor Hansen

Notes & Tasks

Take note of the little things... you will learn that details do count.

Date ______________________

		✓

Remember *Dry Cleaning ... Movie Rentals ... Reservations ... Special Events ... and a whole lot more!*

MONTH OF ____________________

DID THE EARTH MOVE FOR YOU?

Eleven-year-old Angela was stricken with a debilitating disease involving her nervous system. She was unable to walk and her movement was restricted in other ways as well. The doctors did not hold out much hope of her ever recovering from this illness. They predicted she'd spend the rest of her life in a wheelchair. They said that few, if any, were able to come back to normal after contracting this disease. The little girl was undaunted. There, lying in her hospital bed, she would vow to anyone who'd listen that she was definitely going to be walking again someday.

She was transferred to a specialized rehabilitation hospital in the San Francisco Bay area. Whatever therapies could be applied to her case were used. The therapists were charmed by her undefeatable spirit. They taught her about *imaging* -- about seeing herself walking. If it would do nothing else, it would at least give her hope and something positive to do in the long waking hours in her bed. Angela would work as hard as possible in physical therapy, in whirlpools and in exercise sessions. But she worked just as hard lying there faithfully doing her imaging, visualizing herself moving, moving, moving!

One day, as she was straining with all her might to imagine her legs moving again, it seemed though a miracle happened: The bed moved! It began to move around the room! She screamed out, "Look what I'm doing! Look! Look! I can do it! I moved, *I moved!*"

Of course, at this very moment everyone else in the hospital was screaming, too, and running for cover. People were screaming, equipment was falling and glass was breaking. You see, it was the recent San Francisco earthquake. But don't tell that to Angela. She's convinced that she did it. And now only a few years later, she's back in school. On her own two legs. No crutches, no wheelchair. You see, anyone who can shake the earth between San Francisco and Oakland can conquer a piddling little disease, can't they?

Hanoch McCarty

THINGS TO DO

Sunday	Monday	Tuesday

NOTES

Note special events to secure their memory

Month

Wednesday	Thursday	Friday	Saturday

NOTES

Chicken Soup for the Soul ®

CONSIDER THIS

*Richard Hooker worked for seven years on his humorous war novel, M*A*S*H, only to have it rejected by 21 publishers before Morrow decided to publish it. It became a runaway bestseller, spawning a blockbusting movie and a highly successful television series.*

Jack Canfield & Mark Victor Hansen

Notes & Tasks

Take note of the little things...
you will learn that details do count.

Date ______________________

✓

Remember *Dry Cleaning ... Movie Rentals ... Reservations ... Special Events ... and a whole lot more!*

MONTH OF ____________________

THE PASSIONATE PURSUIT OF POSSIBILITY

Years ago, while unearthing an ancient Egyptian tomb, an archaeologist came upon seeds buried in a piece of wood. Planted, the seeds realized their potential after more than 3,000 years! Are there conditions in the lives of people so discouraging, so defeating, that human beings--regardless of inherent potentiality--are doomed to lives of failure and quiet desperation? Or are there also seeds of possibility in people, an urge for becoming that is so strong that the hard crust of adversity is breached? Consider this story that came over the wires of the Associated Press on May 23, 1984:

As a child, Mary Groda did not learn to read and write. Experts labeled her retarded. As an adolescent, she "earned" an additional label, "incorrigible," and was sentenced to two years reformatory. It was here, ironically, in this closed-in place, that Mary--bending to the challenge to learn--worked at her task for as long as 16 hours a day. Her hard work paid off: She was awarded her (GED) high school diploma.

But more misfortune was to visit Mary Groda. After leaving the reformatory, she became pregnant without benefit of marriage. Then, two years later a second pregnancy resulted in a stroke, erasing her hard-earned powers of reading and writing. With the help and support of her father, Mary battled back, regaining what she had lost.

In dire financial straights, Mary went on welfare. Finally, to make ends meet, she took in seven foster children. It was during this period that she started taking courses at a community college. Upon completion of her course work, she applied to and was accepted by the Albany Medical School to study medicine.

In the spring of 1984 in Oregon, Mary Groda Lewis--she's married now--paraded in full academic regalia across the graduation stage. No one can know what private thoughts went through Mary's mind as she reached out to grasp this eloquent testimony to her self-belief and perseverance, her diploma that announced to all the world: Here stands on this small point of Planet Earth a person who dared to dream the impossible dream, a person who confirms for all of us our human divineness. Here stands Mary Groda Lewis, M.D.

James Elwood Conner

THINGS TO DO

Sunday	Monday	Tuesday

NOTES

Note special events to secure their memory

Month

Wednesday	Thursday	Friday	Saturday

NOTES

Chicken Soup for the Soul ®

CONSIDER THIS

After having lost both legs in an air crash, British fighter pilot Douglas Bader rejoined the British Royal Air Force with two artificial limbs. During World War II he was captured by the Germans three times–and three times he escaped.

Jack Canfield & Mark Victor Hansen

Notes & Tasks

*Take note of the little things...
you will learn that details do count.*

Date ______________________________

✓

Remember *Dry Cleaning ... Movie Rentals ... Reservations ... Special Events ... and a whole lot more!*

MONTH OF ______________________

THE GIVING TREES

I was a single parent of four small children, working at a minimum-wage job. Money was always tight, but we had a roof over our heads, food on the table, clothes on our backs and, if not a lot, always enough. My kids told me that in those days they didn't know we were poor. They just thought Mom was cheap. I've always been glad about that.

It was Christmas time, and although there wasn't money for a lot of gifts, we planned to celebrate with church and family, parties and friends, drives downtown to see the Christmas lights, special dinners, and by decorating our home.

But the big excitement for the kids was the fun of Christmas shopping at the mall. They talked and planned for weeks ahead of time, asking each other and their grandparents what they wanted for Christmas. I dreaded it. I had saved $120 for presents to be shared by all five of us.

The big day arrived and we started out early. I gave each of the four kids a twenty dollar bill and reminded them to look for gifts about four dollars each. Then everyone scattered. We had two hours to shop; then we would meet back at the "Santa's workshop" display.

Back in the car driving home, everyone was in high Christmas spirits, laughing and teasing each other with hints and clues about what they had bought. My younger daughter, Ginger, who was about eight years old, was unusually quiet. I noted she had only one small, flat bag with her after her shopping spree. I could see enough through the plastic bag to tell she had bought candy bars--fifty-cent candy bars! I was so angry. *What did you do with that twenty dollar bill I gave you?* I wanted to yell at her, but I didn't say anything until we got home. I called her into my bedroom and closed the door, ready to be angry again when I asked her what she had done with the money. This is what she told me:

"I was looking around, thinking of what to buy, and I stopped to read the little cards on one of the Salvation Army's 'Giving Trees.' One of the cards was for a little girl, four years old, and all she wanted for Christmas was a doll with clothes and a hairbrush. So I took the card off the tree and bought the doll and the hairbrush for her and took it to the Salvation Army booth."

"I only had enough money left to buy candy bars for us," Ginger continued. "But we have so much and she doesn't have anything."

I never felt so rich as I did that day.

Kathleen Dixon

THINGS TO DO

Sunday	Monday	Tuesday

NOTES

Note special events to secure their memory

Month

Wednesday	Thursday	Friday	Saturday

NOTES

Chicken Soup for the Soul ®

CONSIDER THIS

In 1905, the University of Bern turned down a doctoral dissertation as being irrelevant and fanciful. The young physics student who wrote the dissertation was Albert Einstein, who was disappointed but not defeated.

Jack Canfield & Mark Victor Hansen

Notes & Tasks

*Take note of the little things...
you will learn that details do count.*

Date ______________________

		✓

Remember *Dry Cleaning ... Movie Rentals ... Reservations ... Special Events ... and a whole lot more!*

VICTORY LOG

VICTORY LOG

ARE YOU STRONG ENOUGH TO HANDLE CRITICS?

It is not the critic who counts, not the man who points out how the strong man stumbles or where the doer of deeds could have done them better. The credit belongs to the man who is actually in the arena, whose face is marred by dust and sweat and blood, who strives valiantly, who errs and comes short again and again because there is no effort without error and shortcomings, who knows the great devotion, who spends himself in a worthy cause, who at best knows in the end the high achievement of triumph and who at worst, if he fails while daring greatly, knows his place shall never be with those timid and cold souls who know neither victory nor defeat.

Theodore Roosevelt

VICTORY LOG

"Ever since he created his new victory dance we've had to renovate."

Chicken Soup for the Soul® **CONSIDER THIS**

After Fred Astaire's first screen test, the memo from the testing director of MGM, dated 1933, said, "Can't act! Slightly bald! Can dance a little!" Astaire kept that memo over the fireplace in his Beverly Hills home.

Jack Canfield & Mark Victor Hansen

Steps to Success 1

- *Acknowledge the positive past.*
- *Heal and forgive.*

Jack Canfield

Victory Log

#	Victory / Accomplishment	Chip ✓
	Total # of Chips	

My Reward:

Victory Log

Steps to Success 2

- *Use positive self talk.*
- *Affirm your strength and assets.*

Jack Canfield

#	Victory / Accomplishment	Chip
	Total # of Chips	

My Reward: ____

____

Steps to Success 3

- *Clarify your purpose and mission.*
- *Share your vision with others.*

Jack Canfield

Victory Log

#	Victory / Accomplishment	Chip
	Total # of Chips	

My Reward: ____

____

Victory Log

Steps to Success 4
- *Plan your future.*
- *Set goals and objectives.*

Jack Canfield

#	Victory / Accomplishment	Chip
	Total # of Chips	

My Reward:

Steps to Success 5

- *Visualize and affirm your desired outcome.*
- *Act to create it.*

Jack Canfield

Victory Log

#	Victory / Accomplishment	Chip
	Total # of Chips	

My Reward: ____

____

Victory Log

Steps to Success 6

- *Take action and respond to feedback positively.*
- *Take corrective action when you're off course.*

Jack Canfield

#	Victory / Accomplishment	Chip
	Total # of Chips	

My Reward:

Steps to Success 7

- *Persevere and never give up!.*
- *Keep on keeping on.*

Jack Canfield

Victory Log

#	Victory / Accomplishment	Chip
	Total # of Chips	

My Reward: ______________________________

____

Victory Log

Steps to Success 8

- *Celebrate your success and reap the rewards.*
- *Credit the people around you.*

Jack Canfield

#	Victory / Accomplishment	Chip
	Total # of Chips	

My Reward:____

____

Steps to Success 1

- *Acknowledge the positive past.*
- *Heal and forgive.*

Jack Canfield

Victory Log

#	Victory / Accomplishment	Chip
	Total # of Chips	

My Reward:

Victory Log

Steps to Success 2

- *Use positive self talk.*
- *Affirm your strength and assets.*

Jack Canfield

#	Victory / Accomplishment	Chip
	Total # of Chips	

My Reward: ______________________________

Steps to Success 3

- *Clarify your purpose and mission.*
- *Share your vision with others.*

Jack Canfield

Victory Log

#	Victory / Accomplishment	Chip
	Total # of Chips	

My Reward: ____

____

Victory Log

Steps to Success 4

- *Plan your future.*
- *Set goals and objectives.*

Jack Canfield

#	Victory / Accomplishment	Chip
	Total # of Chips	

My Reward: ______________________________

CHICKEN SOUP MOMENTS

CHICKEN SOUP MOMENTS

THE COOKIE THIEF

A woman was waiting at an airport one night,
With several long hours before her flight.
She hunted for a book in the airport shop,
Bought a bag of cookies and found a place to drop.

She was engrossed in her book, but happened to see,
That the man beside her, as bold as could be,
Grabbed a cookie or two from the bag between,
Which she tried to ignore, to avoid a scene.

She read, munched cookies, and watched the clock,
As the gutsy "cookie thief" diminished her stock.
She was getting more irritated as the minutes ticked by,
Thinking, "If I wasn't so nice, I'd blacken his eye!"

With each cookie she took, he took one too.
When only one was left, she wondered what he'd do.
With a smile on his face and a nervous laugh,
He took the last cookie and broke it in half.

He offered her half, as he ate the other.
She snatched it from him and thought, "Oh brother,
This guy has some nerve, and he's also *rude*,
Why, he didn't even show any gratitude!"

She had never known when she had been so galled,
And sighed with relief when her flight was called.
She gathered her belongings and headed for the gate,
Refusing to look back at the "thieving ingrate."

She boarded the plane and sank in her seat,
Then sought her book, which was almost complete.
As she reached in her baggage, she gasped with surprise.
There was her bag of cookies in front of her eyes!

"If mine are here," she moaned with despair,
"Then the others were *his* and he tried to share!"
Too late to apologize, she realized with grief,
That *she* was the rude one, the ingrate, the thief!

Valerie Cox

CHICKEN SOUP MOMENTS

"Aw come on mom, take a break—don't you know Newton was inspired snoozing under an apple tree!"

Chicken Soup for the Soul®

CONSIDER THIS

Walt Disney was fired by a newspaper editor for lack of ideas. Walt Disney also went bankrupt several times before he built Disneyland.

Jack Canfield & Mark Victor Hansen

A new idea is first condemned as ridiculous, and then dismissed as trivial, until finally it becomes what everybody knows.

William James

Chicken Soup Moments

Date ________________ Event ____

Date ________________ Event ____

Date ________________ Event ____

Date ________________ Event ____

Remember to Note

Who, Where, When and What – was Special?

Chicken Soup Moments

As soon as you feel too old to do a thing, do it!

Margaret Delan

Date ____________ Event ____________________

Date ____________ Event ____________________

Date ____________ Event ____________________

Date ____________ Event ____________________

Remember to Note

Who, Where, When and What – was Special?

Hold every moment sacred.
Give each clarity and meaning,
each the weight of thine awareness...
Thomas Mann

Chicken Soup Moments

Date ____________ Event ____________

Date ____________ Event ____________

Date ____________ Event ____________

Date ____________ Event ____________

Remember to Note

Who, Where, When and What – was Special?

Chicken Soup Moments

When one loves somebody, everything is clear – where to go, what to do – it all takes care of itself and one doesn't have to ask anybody about anything.

Maxim Gork

Date ____________ Event ____________

Date ____________ Event ____________

Date ____________ Event ____________

Date ____________ Event ____________

Remember to Note

Who, Where, When and What – was Special?

She likes stories that make her cry – I think we all do. It's so nice to feel sad or inspired when you're feeling nothing in particular!

Annie Sullivan

Chicken Soup Moments

Date ______________ Event ______________________________

Date ______________ Event ______________________________

Date ______________ Event ______________________________

Date ______________ Event ______________________________

emember to Note

Who, Where, When and What – was Special?

You cannot step into the same river twice.

Heraclitus

Date ____________ **Event** ____________________________

Date ____________ **Event** ____________________________

Date ____________ **Event** ____________________________

Date ____________ **Event** ____________________________

Remember to Note

Who, Where, When and What – was Special?

The time is always right
to do what is right.
Martin Luther King Jr.

Chicken Soup Moments

Date ____________ Event ______________________________

Date ____________ Event ______________________________

Date ____________ Event ______________________________

Date ____________ Event ______________________________

Remember to Note

Who, Where, When and What – was Special?

Chicken Soup Moments

It is not who is right, but what is right, that is of importance.

Thomas Huxley

Date ____________ Event ____________________________

Date ____________ Event ____________________________

Date ____________ Event ____________________________

Date ____________ Event ____________________________

Remember to Note

Who, Where, When and What – was Special?

"You never know when you're making a memory"

Rickie Lee Jones

Chicken Soup Moments

Date ____________ **Event** ____________

Date ____________ **Event** ____________

Date ____________ **Event** ____________

Date ____________ **Event** ____________

Remember to Note

Who, Where, When and What – was Special?

To be able to look back upon one's past life with satisfaction is to live twice.

Martial

Date ____________ **Event** ____________

Date ____________ **Event** ____________

Date ____________ **Event** ____________

Date ____________ **Event** ____________

Remember to Note

Who, Where, When and What – was Special?

We are each of us angels with only one wing.
And we can only fly embracing each other.
Luciano De Creschenzo

Chicken Soup Moments

Date ______________ Event ______________________________

Date ______________ Event ______________________________

Date ______________ Event ______________________________

Date ______________ Event ______________________________

Remember to Note

Who, Where, When and What – was Special?

Chicken Soup Moments

The opportunity to practice brotherhood presents itself every time you meet a human being.

Jane Wyman

Date ____________ Event ____________________________

Date ____________ Event ____________________________

Date ____________ Event ____________________________

Date ____________ Event ____________________________

Remember to Note

Who, Where, When and What – was Special?

BUDGET PLANNER

BUDGET PLANNER

WHAT YOU ARE IS AS IMPORTANT AS WHAT YOU DO

If you aren't honest with the rest of the world, how can you hope to be honest with yourself? Honesty isn't what you say you believe, it's what you model, encourage, reward and let happen every day.

Come with me for a moment to Oklahoma. One of my friends, proud father Bobby Lewis, was taking his two little boys to play miniature golf. "It's three bucks for you," the attendant drawled, "and three bucks for any kid who's older than six. They get in free if they're six or younger."

Bobby said, "Well, Mikey's three and Jimmy's seven, so I owe you $6.00." The attendant looked surprised. "Hey mister, do you like throwing your money away? you could have told me the big one was only six and saved three bucks. I wouldn't have known the difference."

"Yes," Bobby said, "but the kids would have known the difference."

Daring to take responsibility for your own life requires truthfulness and honesty in all your dealings, both with yourself and with others. As an individual or a company, what you do in private is as important as what you do in public.

Patricia Fripp

BUDGET PLANNER

"...Hmm...so what you're saying is...there's some kind of correlation between our expenses and our income..."

Chicken Soup for the Soul®

CONSIDER THIS

When Peter J. Daniel was in the fourth grade, his teacher, Mrs. Phillips, constantly said, "Peter J. Daniel, you're no good, you're a bad apple and you're never going to amount to anything." Peter was totally illiterate until he was 26. A friend stayed up with him all night and read him a copy of ***Think and Grow Rich.*** *Now he owns the street corners he used to fight on and just published his latest book:*

Mrs. Phillips, You Were Wrong!

Jack Canfield & Mark Victor Hansen

I always try to rub up against money,
for if you rub up against money long enough,
some of it may rub off on you.
Damon (Alfred) Runyon

Budget Plan

GOALS

To Save ______________________
Other ______________________
Other ______________________

INCOME	PRE-TAX	DIVIDENDS	AFTER TAX	% DIFFERENCE LAST YEAR
Yours				
Spouse / 2nd				

BUDGET	MAIN AREAS	PROJECTED	ACTUAL	+/-
SAVINGS	Savings			
"Must Do First"	RRSP/IRA			
	Investments			
	Education			
	Life Insurance			
	Other			
	SUB-TOTAL			
DEBT / FINANCIAL	Mortgage, Rent, Fees			
	Auto Loan / Lease			
	Loan			
	Credit Card			
	Credit Card			
	Donations			
	Other			
	SUB-TOTAL			
HOUSEHOLD	Property Insurance			
	Maintenance			
	Yard			
	Utilities			
	Telephone			
	Cable TV			
	Food & Supplies			
	Laundry/Dry Cleaning			
	Cleaning Service			
	Other			
	SUB-TOTAL			
AUTO / TRANSIT	Insurance, Permit			
	Maintenance			
	Gas / Oil / Wash			
	Parking			
	Transit, Taxi			
	Other			
	SUB-TOTAL			
MYSELF	Personal Care			
	Clothes			
	Lunches			
	Other			
	SUB-TOTAL			

Keys to Budgeting

Always Pay Yourself First • Target at Least 10% for Savings • Set Realistic Goals

Budget Plan

Pay yourself first and your savings are guaranteed to grow!
James Spratley

BUDGET (continued)

	MAIN AREAS	PROJECTED	ACTUAL	+/-
SPOUSE	Personal Care			
	Clothes			
	Lunches			
	Other			
	SUB-TOTAL			
DEPENDENTS	Daycare			
	Personal Care			
	Babysitters			
	Clothes			
	Lunches			
	Allowances			
	Other			
	SUB-TOTAL			
HEALTH CARE	Hospital Plan			
	Dental Plan			
	Dental			
	Doctor			
	Prescriptions			
	Health Club			
	Other			
	SUB-TOTAL			
OCCASIONS	Christmas			
	Birthdays			
	Anniversaries			
	Valentine's Day			
	Mother & Father's Day			
	Special			
	Other			
	SUB-TOTAL			
LEISURE	Dining			
	Shows/ Movies/ Sports			
	Vacations			
	Hobbies			
	Recreation			
	Other			
	Other			
	SUB-TOTAL			
SPECIAL PURCHASES	Home Improvements			
	Furniture			
	Appliances			
	Other			
	Other			
	Other			
	SUB-TOTAL			
	TOTAL			

The wise and moral man
Shines like a fire on a hilltop,
Making money like the bee,
Who does not hurt the flower.
The Pali Canon

Budget Plan

GOALS

To Save	
Other	
Other	

INCOME	PRE-TAX	DIVIDENDS	AFTER TAX	% DIFFERENCE LAST YEAR
Yours				
Spouse / 2nd				

BUDGET	MAIN AREAS	PROJECTED	ACTUAL	+/-
SAVINGS *"Must Do First"*	Savings			
	RRSP/IRA			
	Investments			
	Education			
	Life Insurance			
	Other			
	SUB-TOTAL			
DEBT / FINANCIAL	Mortgage, Rent, Fees			
	Auto Loan / Lease			
	Loan			
	Credit Card			
	Credit Card			
	Donations			
	Other			
	SUB-TOTAL			
HOUSEHOLD	Property Insurance			
	Maintenance			
	Yard			
	Utilities			
	Telephone			
	Cable TV			
	Food & Supplies			
	Laundry/Dry Cleaning			
	Cleaning Service			
	Other			
	SUB-TOTAL			
AUTO / TRANSIT	Insurance, Permit			
	Maintenance			
	Gas / Oil / Wash			
	Parking			
	Transit, Taxi			
	Other			
	SUB-TOTAL			
MYSELF	Personal Care			
	Clothes			
	Lunches			
	Other			
	SUB-TOTAL			

Keys to Budgeting

Always Pay Yourself First • *Target at Least 10% for Savings* • *Set Realistic Goals*

Budget Plan

Pay yourself first and your savings are guaranteed to grow!
James Spratley

BUDGET (continued)

	MAIN AREAS	PROJECTED	ACTUAL	+/-
SPOUSE	Personal Care			
	Clothes			
	Lunches			
	Other			
	SUB-TOTAL			
DEPENDENTS	Daycare			
	Personal Care			
	Babysitters			
	Clothes			
	Lunches			
	Allowances			
	Other			
	SUB-TOTAL			
HEALTH CARE	Hospital Plan			
	Dental Plan			
	Dental			
	Doctor			
	Prescriptions			
	Health Club			
	Other			
	SUB-TOTAL			
OCCASIONS	Christmas			
	Birthdays			
	Anniversaries			
	Valentine's Day			
	Mother & Father's Day			
	Special			
	Other			
	SUB-TOTAL			
LEISURE	Dining			
	Shows/ Movies/ Sports			
	Vacations			
	Hobbies			
	Recreation			
	Other			
	Other			
	SUB-TOTAL			
SPECIAL PURCHASES	Home Improvements			
	Furniture			
	Appliances			
	Other			
	Other			
	Other			
	SUB-TOTAL			
	TOTAL			

Money is like muck,
not good except it be spread.
Francis Bacon

Budget Plan

GOALS

To Save	
Other	
Other	

INCOME	PRE-TAX	DIVIDENDS	AFTER TAX	% DIFFERENCE LAST YEAR
Yours				
Spouse / 2nd				

BUDGET	MAIN AREAS	PROJECTED	ACTUAL	+/-
SAVINGS	Savings			
"Must Do First"	RRSP/IRA			
	Investments			
	Education			
	Life Insurance			
	Other			
	SUB-TOTAL			
DEBT / FINANCIAL	Mortgage, Rent, Fees			
	Auto Loan / Lease			
	Loan			
	Credit Card			
	Credit Card			
	Donations			
	Other			
	SUB-TOTAL			
HOUSEHOLD	Property Insurance			
	Maintenance			
	Yard			
	Utilities			
	Telephone			
	Cable TV			
	Food & Supplies			
	Laundry/Dry Cleaning			
	Cleaning Service			
	Other			
	SUB-TOTAL			
AUTO / TRANSIT	Insurance, Permit			
	Maintenance			
	Gas / Oil / Wash			
	Parking			
	Transit, Taxi			
	Other			
	SUB-TOTAL			
MYSELF	Personal Care			
	Clothes			
	Lunches			
	Other			
	SUB-TOTAL			

Keys to Budgeting

Always Pay Yourself First • Target at Least 10% for Savings • Set Realistic Goals

Budget Plan

Pay yourself first and your savings are guaranteed to grow!
James Spratley

BUDGET (continued)

	MAIN AREAS	PROJECTED	ACTUAL	+/-
SPOUSE	Personal Care			
	Clothes			
	Lunches			
	Other			
	SUB-TOTAL			
DEPENDENTS	Daycare			
	Personal Care			
	Babysitters			
	Clothes			
	Lunches			
	Allowances			
	Other			
	SUB-TOTAL			
HEALTH CARE	Hospital Plan			
	Dental Plan			
	Dental			
	Doctor			
	Prescriptions			
	Health Club			
	Other			
	SUB-TOTAL			
OCCASIONS	Christmas			
	Birthdays			
	Anniversaries			
	Valentine's Day			
	Mother & Father's Day			
	Special			
	Other			
	SUB-TOTAL			
LEISURE	Dining			
	Shows/ Movies/ Sports			
	Vacations			
	Hobbies			
	Recreation			
	Other			
	Other			
	SUB-TOTAL			
SPECIAL PURCHASES	Home Improvements			
	Furniture			
	Appliances			
	Other			
	Other			
	Other			
	SUB-TOTAL			
	TOTAL			

Budget Plan

Money begets money.
John Ray

GOALS

To Save	
Other	
Other	

INCOME	PRE-TAX	DIVIDENDS	AFTER TAX	% DIFFERENCE LAST YEAR
Yours				
Spouse / 2nd				

BUDGET	MAIN AREAS	PROJECTED	ACTUAL	+/-
SAVINGS	Savings			
"Must Do First"	RRSP/IRA			
	Investments			
	Education			
	Life Insurance			
	Other			
	SUB-TOTAL			
DEBT / FINANCIAL	Mortgage, Rent, Fees			
	Auto Loan / Lease			
	Loan			
	Credit Card			
	Credit Card			
	Donations			
	Other			
	SUB-TOTAL			
HOUSEHOLD	Property Insurance			
	Maintenance			
	Yard			
	Utilities			
	Telephone			
	Cable TV			
	Food & Supplies			
	Laundry/Dry Cleaning			
	Cleaning Service			
	Other			
	SUB-TOTAL			
AUTO / TRANSIT	Insurance, Permit			
	Maintenance			
	Gas / Oil / Wash			
	Parking			
	Transit, Taxi			
	Other			
	SUB-TOTAL			
MYSELF	Personal Care			
	Clothes			
	Lunches			
	Other			
	SUB-TOTAL			

Keys to Budgeting

Always Pay Yourself First • *Target at Least 10% for Savings* • *Set Realistic Goals*

Budget Plan

Pay yourself first and your savings are guaranteed to grow!
James Spratley

BUDGET (continued)

	Main Areas	Projected	Actual	+/-
Spouse	Personal Care			
	Clothes			
	Lunches			
	Other			
	SUB-TOTAL			
Dependents	Daycare			
	Personal Care			
	Babysitters			
	Clothes			
	Lunches			
	Allowances			
	Other			
	SUB-TOTAL			
Health Care	Hospital Plan			
	Dental Plan			
	Dental			
	Doctor			
	Prescriptions			
	Health Club			
	Other			
	SUB-TOTAL			
Occasions	Christmas			
	Birthdays			
	Anniversaries			
	Valentine's Day			
	Mother & Father's Day			
	Special			
	Other			
	SUB-TOTAL			
Leisure	Dining			
	Shows/ Movies/ Sports			
	Vacations			
	Hobbies			
	Recreation			
	Other			
	Other			
	SUB-TOTAL			
Special Purchases	Home Improvements			
	Furniture			
	Appliances			
	Other			
	Other			
	Other			
	SUB-TOTAL			
	TOTAL			

Money is the seed of money, and the first guinea is sometimes more difficult to acquire than the second million.
Jean Jacques Rousseau

Budget Plan

GOALS

To Save ______

Other ______

Other ______

INCOME	PRE-TAX	DIVIDENDS	AFTER TAX	% DIFFERENCE LAST YEAR
Yours				
Spouse / 2nd				

BUDGET	MAIN AREAS	PROJECTED	ACTUAL	+/-
SAVINGS	Savings			
"Must Do First"	RRSP/IRA			
	Investments			
	Education			
	Life Insurance			
	Other			
	SUB-TOTAL			
DEBT / FINANCIAL	Mortgage, Rent, Fees			
	Auto Loan / Lease			
	Loan			
	Credit Card			
	Credit Card			
	Donations			
	Other			
	SUB-TOTAL			
HOUSEHOLD	Property Insurance			
	Maintenance			
	Yard			
	Utilities			
	Telephone			
	Cable TV			
	Food & Supplies			
	Laundry/Dry Cleaning			
	Cleaning Service			
	Other			
	SUB-TOTAL			
AUTO / TRANSIT	Insurance, Permit			
	Maintenance			
	Gas / Oil / Wash			
	Parking			
	Transit, Taxi			
	Other			
	SUB-TOTAL			
MYSELF	Personal Care			
	Clothes			
	Lunches			
	Other			
	SUB-TOTAL			

Keys to Budgeting

Always Pay Yourself First • Target at Least 10% for Savings • Set Realistic Goals

Budget Plan

Pay yourself first and your savings are guaranteed to grow!
James Spratley

BUDGET (continued)

	MAIN AREAS	PROJECTED	ACTUAL	+/-
SPOUSE	Personal Care			
	Clothes			
	Lunches			
	Other			
	SUB-TOTAL			
DEPENDENTS	Daycare			
	Personal Care			
	Babysitters			
	Clothes			
	Lunches			
	Allowances			
	Other			
	SUB-TOTAL			
HEALTH CARE	Hospital Plan			
	Dental Plan			
	Dental			
	Doctor			
	Prescriptions			
	Health Club			
	Other			
	SUB-TOTAL			
OCCASIONS	Christmas			
	Birthdays			
	Anniversaries			
	Valentine's Day			
	Mother & Father's Day			
	Special			
	Other			
	SUB-TOTAL			
LEISURE	Dining			
	Shows/ Movies/ Sports			
	Vacations			
	Hobbies			
	Recreation			
	Other			
	Other			
	SUB-TOTAL			
SPECIAL PURCHASES	Home Improvements			
	Furniture			
	Appliances			
	Other			
	Other			
	Other			
	SUB-TOTAL			
	TOTAL			

Put not your trust in money,
but put your money in trust.
Oliver Wendell Holmes

Budget Plan

GOALS

To Save	
Other	
Other	

INCOME	PRE-TAX	DIVIDENDS	AFTER TAX	% DIFFERENCE LAST YEAR
Yours				
Spouse / 2nd				

BUDGET	MAIN AREAS	PROJECTED	ACTUAL	+/-
SAVINGS	Savings			
"Must Do First"	RRSP/IRA			
	Investments			
	Education			
	Life Insurance			
	Other			
	SUB-TOTAL			
DEBT / FINANCIAL	Mortgage, Rent, Fees			
	Auto Loan / Lease			
	Loan			
	Credit Card			
	Credit Card			
	Donations			
	Other			
	SUB-TOTAL			
HOUSEHOLD	Property Insurance			
	Maintenance			
	Yard			
	Utilities			
	Telephone			
	Cable TV			
	Food & Supplies			
	Laundry/Dry Cleaning			
	Cleaning Service			
	Other			
	SUB-TOTAL			
AUTO / TRANSIT	Insurance, Permit			
	Maintenance			
	Gas / Oil / Wash			
	Parking			
	Transit, Taxi			
	Other			
	SUB-TOTAL			
MYSELF	Personal Care			
	Clothes			
	Lunches			
	Other			
	SUB-TOTAL			

Keys to Budgeting

Always Pay Yourself First • *Target at Least 10% for Savings* • *Set Realistic Goals*

Budget Plan

Pay yourself first and your savings are guaranteed to grow!
James Spratley

BUDGET (continued)

	Main Areas	Projected	Actual	+/-
Spouse	Personal Care			
	Clothes			
	Lunches			
	Other			
	SUB-TOTAL			
Dependents	Daycare			
	Personal Care			
	Babysitters			
	Clothes			
	Lunches			
	Allowances			
	Other			
	SUB-TOTAL			
Health Care	Hospital Plan			
	Dental Plan			
	Dental			
	Doctor			
	Prescriptions			
	Health Club			
	Other			
	SUB-TOTAL			
Occasions	Christmas			
	Birthdays			
	Anniversaries			
	Valentine's Day			
	Mother & Father's Day			
	Special			
	Other			
	SUB-TOTAL			
Leisure	Dining			
	Shows/ Movies/ Sports			
	Vacations			
	Hobbies			
	Recreation			
	Other			
	Other			
	SUB-TOTAL			
Special Purchases	Home Improvements			
	Furniture			
	Appliances			
	Other			
	Other			
	Other			
	SUB-TOTAL			
	TOTAL			

A fool and his money are soon parted.
English Proverb

Budget Plan

GOALS

To Save	
Other	
Other	

INCOME	PRE-TAX	DIVIDENDS	AFTER TAX	% DIFFERENCE LAST YEAR
Yours				
Spouse / 2nd				

BUDGET	MAIN AREAS	PROJECTED	ACTUAL	+/-
SAVINGS	Savings			
"Must Do First"	RRSP/IRA			
	Investments			
	Education			
	Life Insurance			
	Other			
	SUB-TOTAL			
DEBT / FINANCIAL	Mortgage, Rent, Fees			
	Auto Loan / Lease			
	Loan			
	Credit Card			
	Credit Card			
	Donations			
	Other			
	SUB-TOTAL			
HOUSEHOLD	Property Insurance			
	Maintenance			
	Yard			
	Utilities			
	Telephone			
	Cable TV			
	Food & Supplies			
	Laundry/Dry Cleaning			
	Cleaning Service			
	Other			
	SUB-TOTAL			
AUTO / TRANSIT	Insurance, Permit			
	Maintenance			
	Gas / Oil / Wash			
	Parking			
	Transit, Taxi			
	Other			
	SUB-TOTAL			
MYSELF	Personal Care			
	Clothes			
	Lunches			
	Other			
	SUB-TOTAL			

Keys to Budgeting *Always Pay Yourself First • Target at Least 10% for Savings • Set Realistic Goals*

Budget Plan

Pay yourself first and your savings are guaranteed to grow!
James Spratley

BUDGET (continued)

	MAIN AREAS	PROJECTED	ACTUAL	+/-
SPOUSE	Personal Care			
	Clothes			
	Lunches			
	Other			
	SUB-TOTAL			
DEPENDENTS	Daycare			
	Personal Care			
	Babysitters			
	Clothes			
	Lunches			
	Allowances			
	Other			
	SUB-TOTAL			
HEALTH CARE	Hospital Plan			
	Dental Plan			
	Dental			
	Doctor			
	Prescriptions			
	Health Club			
	Other			
	SUB-TOTAL			
OCCASIONS	Christmas			
	Birthdays			
	Anniversaries			
	Valentine's Day			
	Mother & Father's Day			
	Special			
	Other			
	SUB-TOTAL			
LEISURE	Dining			
	Shows/ Movies/ Sports			
	Vacations			
	Hobbies			
	Recreation			
	Other			
	Other			
	SUB-TOTAL			
SPECIAL PURCHASES	Home Improvements			
	Furniture			
	Appliances			
	Other			
	Other			
	Other			
	SUB-TOTAL			
	TOTAL			

Money is like a sixth sense without which you cannot make a complete use of the other five.
Amy Lowell

Budget Plan

GOALS

To Save ______________________
Other ______________________
Other ______________________

INCOME	PRE-TAX	DIVIDENDS	AFTER TAX	% DIFFERENCE LAST YEAR
Yours				
Spouse / 2nd				

BUDGET	MAIN AREAS	PROJECTED	ACTUAL	+/-
SAVINGS *"Must Do First"*	Savings			
	RRSP/IRA			
	Investments			
	Education			
	Life Insurance			
	Other			
	SUB-TOTAL			
DEBT / FINANCIAL	Mortgage, Rent, Fees			
	Auto Loan / Lease			
	Loan			
	Credit Card			
	Credit Card			
	Donations			
	Other			
	SUB-TOTAL			
HOUSEHOLD	Property Insurance			
	Maintenance			
	Yard			
	Utilities			
	Telephone			
	Cable TV			
	Food & Supplies			
	Laundry/Dry Cleaning			
	Cleaning Service			
	Other			
	SUB-TOTAL			
AUTO / TRANSIT	Insurance, Permit			
	Maintenance			
	Gas / Oil / Wash			
	Parking			
	Transit, Taxi			
	Other			
	SUB-TOTAL			
MYSELF	Personal Care			
	Clothes			
	Lunches			
	Other			
	SUB-TOTAL			

Keys to Budgeting

Always Pay Yourself First • Target at Least 10% for Savings • Set Realistic Goals

Budget Plan

Pay yourself first and your savings are guaranteed to grow!
James Spratley

BUDGET (continued)

	Main Areas	Projected	Actual	+/-
Spouse	Personal Care			
	Clothes			
	Lunches			
	Other			
	SUB-TOTAL			
Dependents	Daycare			
	Personal Care			
	Babysitters			
	Clothes			
	Lunches			
	Allowances			
	Other			
	SUB-TOTAL			
Health Care	Hospital Plan			
	Dental Plan			
	Dental			
	Doctor			
	Prescriptions			
	Health Club			
	Other			
	SUB-TOTAL			
Occasions	Christmas			
	Birthdays			
	Anniversaries			
	Valentine's Day			
	Mother & Father's Day			
	Special			
	Other			
	SUB-TOTAL			
Leisure	Dining			
	Shows/ Movies/ Sports			
	Vacations			
	Hobbies			
	Recreation			
	Other			
	Other			
	SUB-TOTAL			
Special Purchases	Home Improvements			
	Furniture			
	Appliances			
	Other			
	Other			
	Other			
	SUB-TOTAL			
	TOTAL			

I always try to rub up against money,
for if you rub up against money long enough,
some of it may rub off on you.
Damon (Alfred) Runyon

Budget Plan

GOALS

To Save	
Other	
Other	

INCOME	PRE-TAX	DIVIDENDS	AFTER TAX	% DIFFERENCE LAST YEAR
Yours				
Spouse / 2nd				

BUDGET	MAIN AREAS	PROJECTED	ACTUAL	+/-
SAVINGS *"Must Do First"*	Savings			
	RRSP/IRA			
	Investments			
	Education			
	Life Insurance			
	Other			
	SUB-TOTAL			
DEBT / FINANCIAL	Mortgage, Rent, Fees			
	Auto Loan / Lease			
	Loan			
	Credit Card			
	Credit Card			
	Donations			
	Other			
	SUB-TOTAL			
HOUSEHOLD	Property Insurance			
	Maintenance			
	Yard			
	Utilities			
	Telephone			
	Cable TV			
	Food & Supplies			
	Laundry/Dry Cleaning			
	Cleaning Service			
	Other			
	SUB-TOTAL			
AUTO / TRANSIT	Insurance, Permit			
	Maintenance			
	Gas / Oil / Wash			
	Parking			
	Transit, Taxi			
	Other			
	SUB-TOTAL			
MYSELF	Personal Care			
	Clothes			
	Lunches			
	Other			
	SUB-TOTAL			

Keys to Budgeting — *Always Pay Yourself First* • *Target at Least 10% for Savings* • *Set Realistic Goals*

Budget Plan

Pay yourself first and your savings are guaranteed to grow!
James Spratley

BUDGET (continued)

	MAIN AREAS	PROJECTED	ACTUAL	+/-
SPOUSE	Personal Care			
	Clothes			
	Lunches			
	Other			
	SUB-TOTAL			
DEPENDENTS	Daycare			
	Personal Care			
	Babysitters			
	Clothes			
	Lunches			
	Allowances			
	Other			
	SUB-TOTAL			
HEALTH CARE	Hospital Plan			
	Dental Plan			
	Dental			
	Doctor			
	Prescriptions			
	Health Club			
	Other			
	SUB-TOTAL			
OCCASIONS	Christmas			
	Birthdays			
	Anniversaries			
	Valentine's Day			
	Mother & Father's Day			
	Special			
	Other			
	SUB-TOTAL			
LEISURE	Dining			
	Shows/ Movies/ Sports			
	Vacations			
	Hobbies			
	Recreation			
	Other			
	Other			
	SUB-TOTAL			
SPECIAL PURCHASES	Home Improvements			
	Furniture			
	Appliances			
	Other			
	Other			
	Other			
	SUB-TOTAL			
	TOTAL			

The wise and moral man
Shines like a fire on a hilltop,
Making money like the bee,
Who does not hurt the flower.
The Pali Canon

Budget Plan

GOALS

To Save	
Other	
Other	

INCOME	PRE-TAX	DIVIDENDS	AFTER TAX	% DIFFERENCE LAST YEAR
Yours				
Spouse / 2nd				

BUDGET	MAIN AREAS	PROJECTED	ACTUAL	+/-
SAVINGS	Savings			
"Must Do First"	RRSP/IRA			
	Investments			
	Education			
	Life Insurance			
	Other			
	SUB-TOTAL			
DEBT / FINANCIAL	Mortgage, Rent, Fees			
	Auto Loan / Lease			
	Loan			
	Credit Card			
	Credit Card			
	Donations			
	Other			
	SUB-TOTAL			
HOUSEHOLD	Property Insurance			
	Maintenance			
	Yard			
	Utilities			
	Telephone			
	Cable TV			
	Food & Supplies			
	Laundry/Dry Cleaning			
	Cleaning Service			
	Other			
	SUB-TOTAL			
AUTO / TRANSIT	Insurance, Permit			
	Maintenance			
	Gas / Oil / Wash			
	Parking			
	Transit, Taxi			
	Other			
	SUB-TOTAL			
MYSELF	Personal Care			
	Clothes			
	Lunches			
	Other			
	SUB-TOTAL			

Always Pay Yourself First • Target at Least 10% for Savings • Set Realistic Goals

Budget Plan

Pay yourself first and your savings are guaranteed to grow!
James Spratley

BUDGET (continued)

	Main Areas	Projected	Actual	+/-
Spouse	Personal Care			
	Clothes			
	Lunches			
	Other			
	Sub-Total			
Dependents	Daycare			
	Personal Care			
	Babysitters			
	Clothes			
	Lunches			
	Allowances			
	Other			
	Sub-Total			
Health Care	Hospital Plan			
	Dental Plan			
	Dental			
	Doctor			
	Prescriptions			
	Health Club			
	Other			
	Sub-Total			
Occasions	Christmas			
	Birthdays			
	Anniversaries			
	Valentine's Day			
	Mother & Father's Day			
	Special			
	Other			
	Sub-Total			
Leisure	Dining			
	Shows/ Movies/ Sports			
	Vacations			
	Hobbies			
	Recreation			
	Other			
	Other			
	Sub-Total			
Special Purchases	Home Improvements			
	Furniture			
	Appliances			
	Other			
	Other			
	Other			
	Sub-Total			
	TOTAL			

Money is like muck,
not good except it be spread.
Francis Bacon

Budget Plan

GOALS

To Save ______________________

Other ______________________

Other ______________________

INCOME	PRE-TAX	DIVIDENDS	AFTER TAX	% DIFFERENCE LAST YEAR
Yours				
Spouse / 2nd				

BUDGET	MAIN AREAS	PROJECTED	ACTUAL	+/-
SAVINGS	Savings			
"Must Do First"	RRSP/IRA			
	Investments			
	Education			
	Life Insurance			
	Other			
	SUB-TOTAL			
DEBT / FINANCIAL	Mortgage, Rent, Fees			
	Auto Loan / Lease			
	Loan			
	Credit Card			
	Credit Card			
	Donations			
	Other			
	SUB-TOTAL			
HOUSEHOLD	Property Insurance			
	Maintenance			
	Yard			
	Utilities			
	Telephone			
	Cable TV			
	Food & Supplies			
	Laundry/Dry Cleaning			
	Cleaning Service			
	Other			
	SUB-TOTAL			
AUTO / TRANSIT	Insurance, Permit			
	Maintenance			
	Gas / Oil / Wash			
	Parking			
	Transit, Taxi			
	Other			
	SUB-TOTAL			
MYSELF	Personal Care			
	Clothes			
	Lunches			
	Other			
	SUB-TOTAL			

Keys to Budgeting

Always Pay Yourself First • *Target at Least 10% for Savings* • *Set Realistic Goals*

Budget Plan

Pay yourself first and your savings are guaranteed to grow!
James Spratley

BUDGET (continued)

	MAIN AREAS	PROJECTED	ACTUAL	+/-
SPOUSE	Personal Care			
	Clothes			
	Lunches			
	Other			
	SUB-TOTAL			
DEPENDENTS	Daycare			
	Personal Care			
	Babysitters			
	Clothes			
	Lunches			
	Allowances			
	Other			
	SUB-TOTAL			
HEALTH CARE	Hospital Plan			
	Dental Plan			
	Dental			
	Doctor			
	Prescriptions			
	Health Club			
	Other			
	SUB-TOTAL			
OCCASIONS	Christmas			
	Birthdays			
	Anniversaries			
	Valentine's Day			
	Mother & Father's Day			
	Special			
	Other			
	SUB-TOTAL			
LEISURE	Dining			
	Shows/ Movies/ Sports			
	Vacations			
	Hobbies			
	Recreation			
	Other			
	Other			
	SUB-TOTAL			
SPECIAL PURCHASES	Home Improvements			
	Furniture			
	Appliances			
	Other			
	Other			
	Other			
	SUB-TOTAL			
	TOTAL			

Budget Plan

Money begets money.
John Ray

GOALS

To Save ______
Other ______
Other ______

INCOME	PRE-TAX	DIVIDENDS	AFTER TAX	% DIFFERENCE LAST YEAR
Yours				
Spouse / 2nd				

BUDGET	MAIN AREAS	PROJECTED	ACTUAL	+/-
SAVINGS *"Must Do First"*	Savings			
	RRSP/IRA			
	Investments			
	Education			
	Life Insurance			
	Other			
	SUB-TOTAL			
DEBT / FINANCIAL	Mortgage, Rent, Fees			
	Auto Loan / Lease			
	Loan			
	Credit Card			
	Credit Card			
	Donations			
	Other			
	SUB-TOTAL			
HOUSEHOLD	Property Insurance			
	Maintenance			
	Yard			
	Utilities			
	Telephone			
	Cable TV			
	Food & Supplies			
	Laundry/Dry Cleaning			
	Cleaning Service			
	Other			
	SUB-TOTAL			
AUTO / TRANSIT	Insurance, Permit			
	Maintenance			
	Gas / Oil / Wash			
	Parking			
	Transit, Taxi			
	Other			
	SUB-TOTAL			
MYSELF	Personal Care			
	Clothes			
	Lunches			
	Other			
	SUB-TOTAL			

Keys to Budgeting

Always Pay Yourself First • Target at Least 10% for Savings • Set Realistic Goals

Budget Plan

Pay yourself first and your savings are guaranteed to grow!
James Spratley

BUDGET (continued)

	Main Areas	Projected	Actual	+/-
Spouse	Personal Care			
	Clothes			
	Lunches			
	Other			
	SUB-TOTAL			
Dependents	Daycare			
	Personal Care			
	Babysitters			
	Clothes			
	Lunches			
	Allowances			
	Other			
	SUB-TOTAL			
Health Care	Hospital Plan			
	Dental Plan			
	Dental			
	Doctor			
	Prescriptions			
	Health Club			
	Other			
	SUB-TOTAL			
Occasions	Christmas			
	Birthdays			
	Anniversaries			
	Valentine's Day			
	Mother & Father's Day			
	Special			
	Other			
	SUB-TOTAL			
Leisure	Dining			
	Shows/ Movies/ Sports			
	Vacations			
	Hobbies			
	Recreation			
	Other			
	Other			
	SUB-TOTAL			
Special Purchases	Home Improvements			
	Furniture			
	Appliances			
	Other			
	Other			
	Other			
	SUB-TOTAL			
	TOTAL			

Money is the seed of money, and the first guinea is sometimes more difficult to acquire than the second million.
Jean Jacques Rousseau

Budget Plan

GOALS

To Save	
Other	
Other	

INCOME	PRE-TAX	DIVIDENDS	AFTER TAX	% DIFFERENCE LAST YEAR
Yours				
Spouse / 2nd				

BUDGET	MAIN AREAS	PROJECTED	ACTUAL	+/-
SAVINGS *"Must Do First"*	Savings			
	RRSP/IRA			
	Investments			
	Education			
	Life Insurance			
	Other			
	SUB-TOTAL			
DEBT / FINANCIAL	Mortgage, Rent, Fees			
	Auto Loan / Lease			
	Loan			
	Credit Card			
	Credit Card			
	Donations			
	Other			
	SUB-TOTAL			
HOUSEHOLD	Property Insurance			
	Maintenance			
	Yard			
	Utilities			
	Telephone			
	Cable TV			
	Food & Supplies			
	Laundry/Dry Cleaning			
	Cleaning Service			
	Other			
	SUB-TOTAL			
AUTO / TRANSIT	Insurance, Permit			
	Maintenance			
	Gas / Oil / Wash			
	Parking			
	Transit, Taxi			
	Other			
	SUB-TOTAL			
MYSELF	Personal Care			
	Clothes			
	Lunches			
	Other			
	SUB-TOTAL			

Keys to Budgeting

Always Pay Yourself First • Target at Least 10% for Savings • Set Realistic Goals

Budget Plan

Pay yourself first and your savings are guaranteed to grow!
James Spratley

BUDGET (continued)

	MAIN AREAS	PROJECTED	ACTUAL	+/-
SPOUSE	Personal Care			
	Clothes			
	Lunches			
	Other			
	SUB-TOTAL			
DEPENDENTS	Daycare			
	Personal Care			
	Babysitters			
	Clothes			
	Lunches			
	Allowances			
	Other			
	SUB-TOTAL			
HEALTH CARE	Hospital Plan			
	Dental Plan			
	Dental			
	Doctor			
	Prescriptions			
	Health Club			
	Other			
	SUB-TOTAL			
OCCASIONS	Christmas			
	Birthdays			
	Anniversaries			
	Valentine's Day			
	Mother & Father's Day			
	Special			
	Other			
	SUB-TOTAL			
LEISURE	Dining			
	Shows/ Movies/ Sports			
	Vacations			
	Hobbies			
	Recreation			
	Other			
	Other			
	SUB-TOTAL			
SPECIAL PURCHASES	Home Improvements			
	Furniture			
	Appliances			
	Other			
	Other			
	Other			
	SUB-TOTAL			
	TOTAL			

Put not your trust in money,
but put your money in trust.
Oliver Wendell Holmes

Budget Plan

GOALS

To Save ______________________
Other ______________________
Other ______________________

INCOME	PRE-TAX	DIVIDENDS	AFTER TAX	% DIFFERENCE LAST YEAR
Yours				
Spouse / 2nd				

BUDGET	MAIN AREAS	PROJECTED	ACTUAL	+/-
SAVINGS *"Must Do First"*	Savings			
	RRSP/IRA			
	Investments			
	Education			
	Life Insurance			
	Other			
	SUB-TOTAL			
DEBT / FINANCIAL	Mortgage, Rent, Fees			
	Auto Loan / Lease			
	Loan			
	Credit Card			
	Credit Card			
	Donations			
	Other			
	SUB-TOTAL			
HOUSEHOLD	Property Insurance			
	Maintenance			
	Yard			
	Utilities			
	Telephone			
	Cable TV			
	Food & Supplies			
	Laundry/Dry Cleaning			
	Cleaning Service			
	Other			
	SUB-TOTAL			
AUTO / TRANSIT	Insurance, Permit			
	Maintenance			
	Gas / Oil / Wash			
	Parking			
	Transit, Taxi			
	Other			
	SUB-TOTAL			
MYSELF	Personal Care			
	Clothes			
	Lunches			
	Other			
	SUB-TOTAL			

Keys to Budgeting

Always Pay Yourself First • Target at Least 10% for Savings • Set Realistic Goals

Budget Plan

Pay yourself first and your savings are guaranteed to grow!
James Spratley

BUDGET (continued)

	Main Areas	Projected	Actual	+/-
Spouse	Personal Care			
	Clothes			
	Lunches			
	Other			
	SUB-TOTAL			
Dependents	Daycare			
	Personal Care			
	Babysitters			
	Clothes			
	Lunches			
	Allowances			
	Other			
	SUB-TOTAL			
Health Care	Hospital Plan			
	Dental Plan			
	Dental			
	Doctor			
	Prescriptions			
	Health Club			
	Other			
	SUB-TOTAL			
Occasions	Christmas			
	Birthdays			
	Anniversaries			
	Valentine's Day			
	Mother & Father's Day			
	Special			
	Other			
	SUB-TOTAL			
Leisure	Dining			
	Shows/ Movies/ Sports			
	Vacations			
	Hobbies			
	Recreation			
	Other			
	Other			
	SUB-TOTAL			
Special Purchases	Home Improvements			
	Furniture			
	Appliances			
	Other			
	Other			
	Other			
	SUB-TOTAL			
	TOTAL			

A fool and his money are
soon parted.
English Proverb

Budget Plan

GOALS

To Save ______________________________
Other ______________________________
Other ______________________________

INCOME	PRE-TAX	DIVIDENDS	AFTER TAX	% DIFFERENCE LAST YEAR
Yours				
Spouse / 2nd				

BUDGET	MAIN AREAS	PROJECTED	ACTUAL	+/-
SAVINGS *"Must Do First"*	Savings			
	RRSP/IRA			
	Investments			
	Education			
	Life Insurance			
	Other			
	SUB-TOTAL			
DEBT / FINANCIAL	Mortgage, Rent, Fees			
	Auto Loan / Lease			
	Loan			
	Credit Card			
	Credit Card			
	Donations			
	Other			
	SUB-TOTAL			
HOUSEHOLD	Property Insurance			
	Maintenance			
	Yard			
	Utilities			
	Telephone			
	Cable TV			
	Food & Supplies			
	Laundry/Dry Cleaning			
	Cleaning Service			
	Other			
	SUB-TOTAL			
AUTO / TRANSIT	Insurance, Permit			
	Maintenance			
	Gas / Oil / Wash			
	Parking			
	Transit, Taxi			
	Other			
	SUB-TOTAL			
MYSELF	Personal Care			
	Clothes			
	Lunches			
	Other			
	SUB-TOTAL			

Keys to Budgeting

Always Pay Yourself First • Target at Least 10% for Savings • Set Realistic Goals

Pay yourself first and your savings are guaranteed to grow!
James Spratley

BUDGET (continued)

	MAIN AREAS	PROJECTED	ACTUAL	+/-
SPOUSE	Personal Care			
	Clothes			
	Lunches			
	Other			
	SUB-TOTAL			
DEPENDENTS	Daycare			
	Personal Care			
	Babysitters			
	Clothes			
	Lunches			
	Allowances			
	Other			
	SUB-TOTAL			
HEALTH CARE	Hospital Plan			
	Dental Plan			
	Dental			
	Doctor			
	Prescriptions			
	Health Club			
	Other			
	SUB-TOTAL			
OCCASIONS	Christmas			
	Birthdays			
	Anniversaries			
	Valentine's Day			
	Mother & Father's Day			
	Special			
	Other			
	SUB-TOTAL			
LEISURE	Dining			
	Shows/ Movies/ Sports			
	Vacations			
	Hobbies			
	Recreation			
	Other			
	Other			
	SUB-TOTAL			
SPECIAL PURCHASES	Home Improvements			
	Furniture			
	Appliances			
	Other			
	Other			
	Other			
	SUB-TOTAL			
	TOTAL			

Money is like a sixth sense without which you cannot make a complete use of the other five.
Amy Lowell

Budget Plan

GOALS

To Save	
Other	
Other	

INCOME	PRE-TAX	DIVIDENDS	AFTER TAX	% DIFFERENCE LAST YEAR
Yours				
Spouse / 2nd				

BUDGET	MAIN AREAS	PROJECTED	ACTUAL	+/-
SAVINGS *"Must Do First"*	Savings			
	RRSP/IRA			
	Investments			
	Education			
	Life Insurance			
	Other			
	SUB-TOTAL			
DEBT / FINANCIAL	Mortgage, Rent, Fees			
	Auto Loan / Lease			
	Loan			
	Credit Card			
	Credit Card			
	Donations			
	Other			
	SUB-TOTAL			
HOUSEHOLD	Property Insurance			
	Maintenance			
	Yard			
	Utilities			
	Telephone			
	Cable TV			
	Food & Supplies			
	Laundry/Dry Cleaning			
	Cleaning Service			
	Other			
	SUB-TOTAL			
AUTO / TRANSIT	Insurance, Permit			
	Maintenance			
	Gas / Oil / Wash			
	Parking			
	Transit, Taxi			
	Other			
	SUB-TOTAL			
MYSELF	Personal Care			
	Clothes			
	Lunches			
	Other			
	SUB-TOTAL			

Keys to Budgeting

Always Pay Yourself First • *Target at Least 10% for Savings* • *Set Realistic Goals*

Budget Plan

Pay yourself first and your savings are guaranteed to grow!
James Spratley

BUDGET (continued)

	MAIN AREAS	PROJECTED	ACTUAL	+/-
SPOUSE	Personal Care			
	Clothes			
	Lunches			
	Other			
	SUB-TOTAL			
DEPENDENTS	Daycare			
	Personal Care			
	Babysitters			
	Clothes			
	Lunches			
	Allowances			
	Other			
	SUB-TOTAL			
HEALTH CARE	Hospital Plan			
	Dental Plan			
	Dental			
	Doctor			
	Prescriptions			
	Health Club			
	Other			
	SUB-TOTAL			
OCCASIONS	Christmas			
	Birthdays			
	Anniversaries			
	Valentine's Day			
	Mother & Father's Day			
	Special			
	Other			
	SUB-TOTAL			
LEISURE	Dining			
	Shows/ Movies/ Sports			
	Vacations			
	Hobbies			
	Recreation			
	Other			
	Other			
	SUB-TOTAL			
SPECIAL PURCHASES	Home Improvements			
	Furniture			
	Appliances			
	Other			
	Other			
	Other			
	SUB-TOTAL			
	TOTAL			

TAKE NOTE

TAKE NOTE

LET'S GO BUG HUNTING MORE OFTEN

One fall afternoon I rushed home from the university where I taught. I prepared a hasty dinner, threatened my nine-year-old daughter, Christi, to hurry and finish her homework "or else", and properly reprimanded Del, my husband, for leaving his dusty shoes on the good carpet. I then frantically vacuumed the entryway because a group of prestigious ladies were coming by to pick up some good used clothing for a worthwhile cause; and then later a graduate student would be at our house to work on a very important thesis—one that I was certain would make a sound contribution to research.

As I paused to catch my breath, I heard Christi talking with a friend on the telephone. Her comments went something like this: "Mom is cleaning house — some ladies we don't even know are coming by to pick up some old worn-out clothes... and a college student is coming out to work on a thesis... no, I don't know what a thesis is... I just know Mom isn't doing anything important... and she won't go bug hunting with me."

Before Christi had hung up the phone, I had put on my jeans and old tennis shoes, persuaded Del to do likewise, pinned a note to the door telling the graduate student I'd be back soon, and set the box of used clothing on the front porch with a note on it that Del, Christi and I had gone bug hunting.

Barbara Chesser, Ph.D.

TAKE NOTE

"Don't worry sir, I've made a note of it."

Chicken Soup for the Soul®

CONSIDER THIS

Babe Ruth, considered by sports historians to be the greatest athlete of all time and famous for setting the home run record, also holds the record for strikeouts.

Jack Canfield & Mark Victor Hansen

Take note of the little things...
you will see clearly what was always there.

Take Note

Date ______________________________

Take Note

Take note of the little things...
you will learn that details do count.

Date ______________________

Take note of the little things...
good things come in small packages.

Take Note

Date ______________________

Take Note

Take note of the little things...
you will learn that details do count.

Date ______________________________

Take note of the little things...
and you may have more fun!

Take Note

Date ______________________

Take Note

Take note of the little things...
you will learn that details do count.

Date ____________________________

*Take note of the little things...
you may be amazed how they
add up to something big!*

Take Note

Date ______________________

Take Note

Take note of the little things...
you will learn that details do count.

Date ____________________

Take note of the little things...
you will forget about big troubles for awhile.

Take Note

Date ______________________________

Take Note

Take note of the little things...
you will learn that details do count.

Date ______________________________

Take note of the little things...
you will feel like a kid again.

Take Note

Date ______________________

Take Note

Take note of the little things...
you will learn that details do count.

Date ______________________________

Take note of the little things...
maybe you'll see life in a different light.

Take Note

Date ______________________________

Take Note

Take note of the little things...
you will learn that details do count.

Date ______________________________

Take note of the little things...
they all add up to the big picture.

Take Note

Date ______________________________

Take Note

Take note of the little things...
you will learn that details do count.

Date ______________________________

Take note of the little things...
you will see clearly what was always there.

Take Note

Date ____________________

Take Note

Take note of the little things...
you will learn that details do count.

Date ______________________

Date ______________________

Take Note

Take note of the little things...
you will learn that details do count.

Date ______________________

Take note of the little things...
and you may have more fun!

Take Note

Date ____________________

Take Note

Take note of the little things...
you will learn that details do count.

Date ___________________________

Take note of the little things...
you may be amazed how they
add up to something big!

Take Note

Date ______________________________

Take Note

Take note of the little things...
you will learn that details do count.

Date ______________________

Take note of the little things...
you will forget about big troubles for awhile.

Take Note

Date ______________________________

Take Note

Take note of the little things...
you will learn that details do count.

Date ______________________

Take note of the little things...
you will feel like a kid again.

Take Note

Date ________________________

Take Note

Take note of the little things...
you will learn that details do count.

Date ______________________

Take note of the little things...
maybe you'll see life in a different light.

Take Note

Date ______________________________

Take Note

Take note of the little things...
you will learn that details do count.

Date ______________________

Take note of the little things...
they all add up to the big picture.

Take Note

Date ______________________

Take Note

*Take note of the little things...
you will learn that details do count.*

Date ____________________

AN ACT OF KINDNESS FOR A BROKEN HEART

My husband, Hanoch, and I wrote a book, *Acts of Kindness: How to Create a Kindness Revolution,* which has generated much interest across America. This story was shared with us by an anonymous caller during a radio talk show in Chicago.

"Hi, Mommy, what are you doing?" asked Susie.

"I'm making a casserole for Mrs. Smith next door," said her mother.

"Why?" asked Susie, who was only six years old.

"Because Mrs. Smith is very sad; she lost her daughter and she has a broken heart. We need to take care of her for a little while."

"Why, Mommy?"

"You see, Susie, when someone is very, very sad, they have trouble doing the little things like making dinner or other chores. Because we're part of a community and Mrs. Smith is our neighbor, we need to do some things to help her. Mrs. Smith won't ever be able to talk with her daughter or hug her or do all those wonderful things that mommies and daughters do together. You are a very smart girl, Susie; maybe you'll think of some way to help take care of Mrs. Smith."

Susie thought seriously about this challenge and how she could do her part in caring for Mrs. Smith. A few minutes later, Susie knocked on her door. After a few moments Mrs. Smith answered the knock with a "Hi, Susie."

Susie noticed that Mrs. Smith didn't have that familiar musical quality about her voice when she greeted someone.

Mrs. Smith also looked as though she might have been crying because her eyes were watery and swollen.

"What can I do for you, Susie?" asked Mrs. Smith.

"My mommy says that you lost your daughter and you're very, very sad with a broken heart." Susie held her hand out shyly. In it was a Band-Aid. "This is for your broken heart." Mrs. Smith gasped, choking back her tears. She knelt down and hugged Susie. Through her tears she said, "Thank you, darling girl, this will help a lot."

Mrs. Smith accepted Susie's act of kindness and took it one step further. She purchased a small key ring with a plexiglass picture frame—the ones designed to carry keys and proudly display a family portrait at the same time. Mrs. Smith placed Susie's Band-Aid in the frame to remind herself to heal a little every time she sees it. She wisely knows that healing takes time and support. It has become her symbol for healing, while not forgetting the joy and love she experienced with her daughter.

Meladee McCarty

A-Z DIRECTORY

"...And this part of the house is dedicated to our teenage daughter Joannie's phone directory."

Chicken Soup for the Soul®

CONSIDER THIS

*Louisa May Alcott, the author of **Little Women,** was encouraged to find work as a servant or seamstress by her family.*

Jack Canfield & Mark Victor Hansen

A
alex Le
B

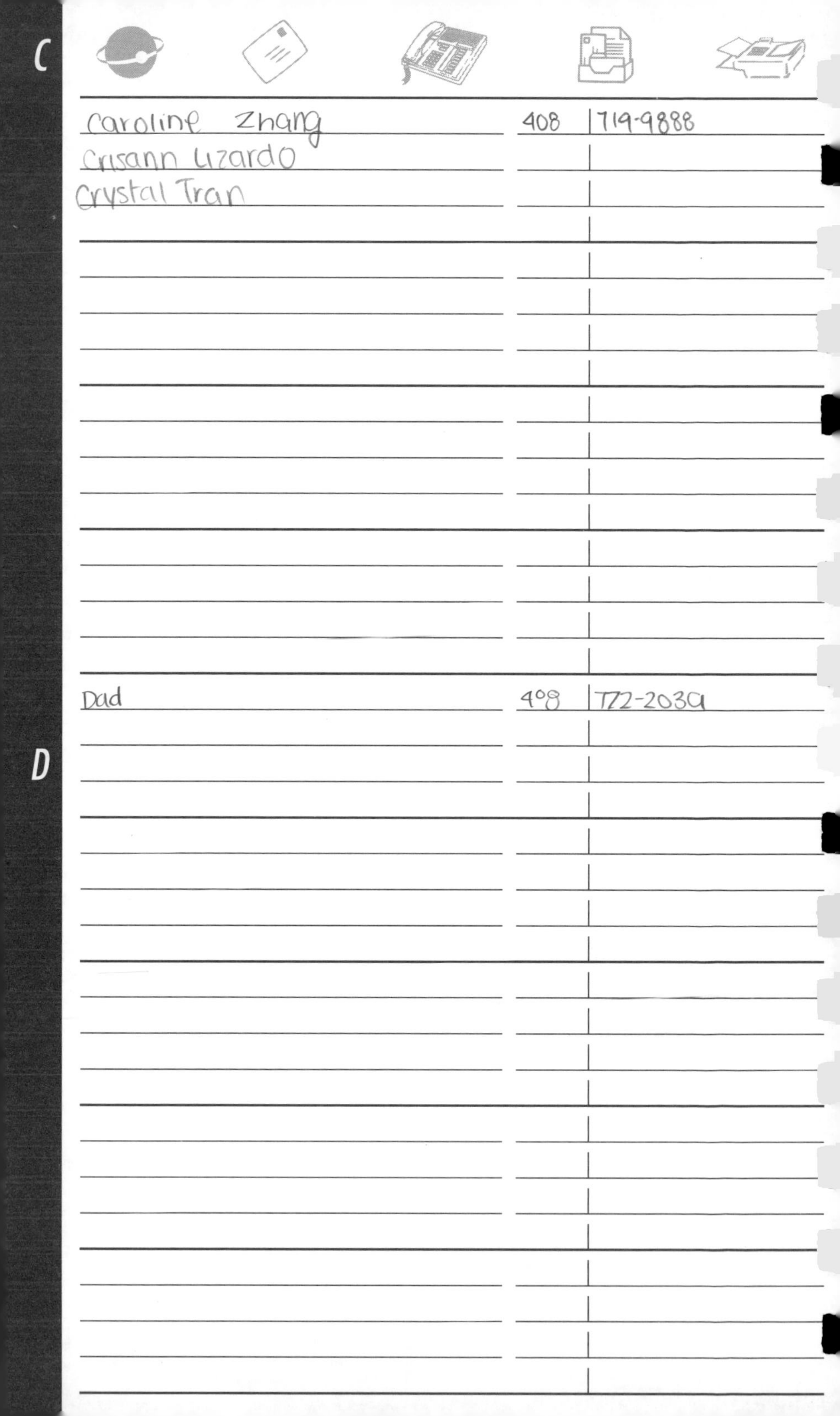
C
Caroline Zhang 408 719-9888
Crisann Lizardo
Crystal Tran
Dad 408 772-2039
D

E
F

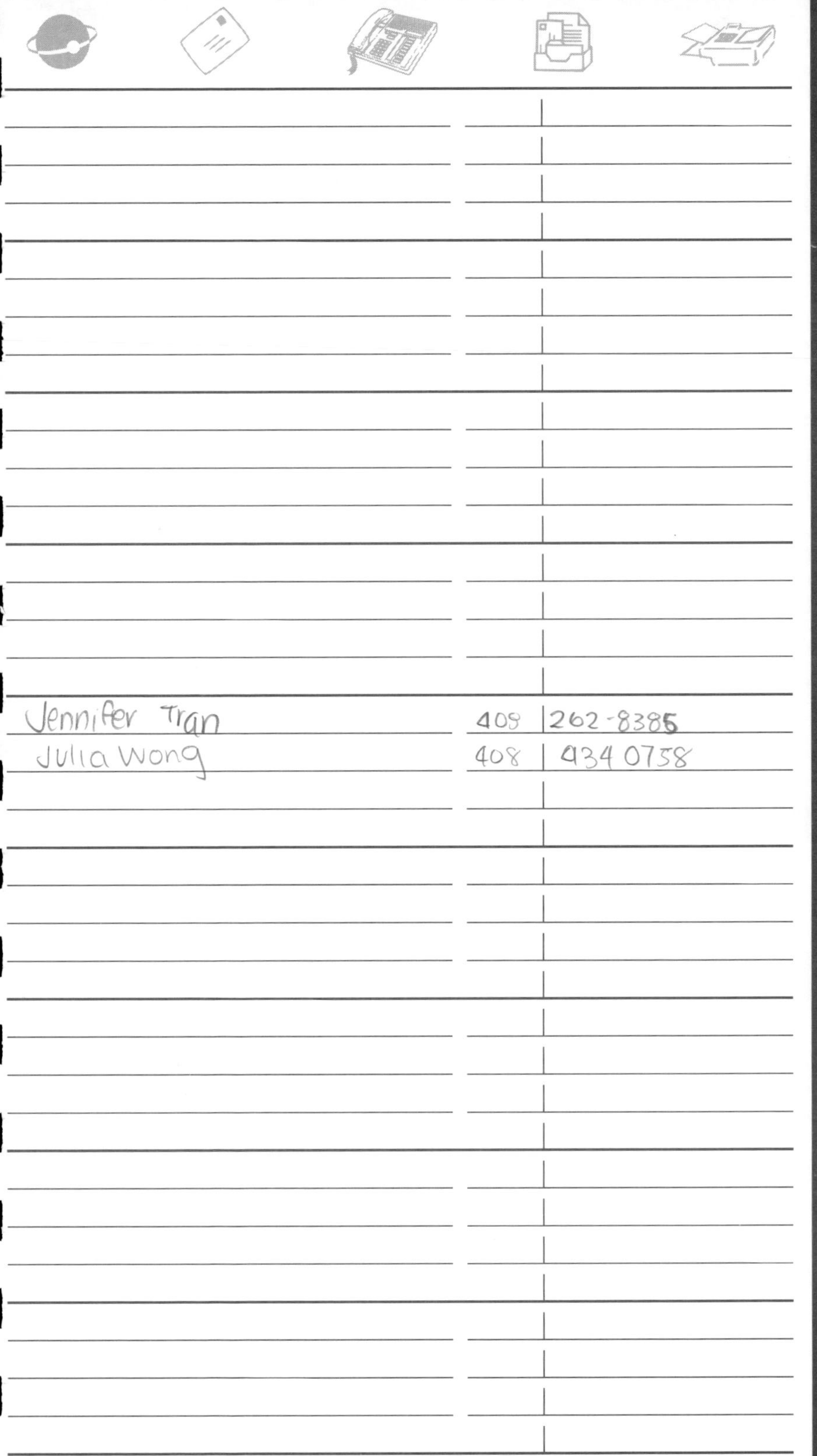
I
Jennifer Tran 408 262-8385
Julia Wong 408 934 0758
J

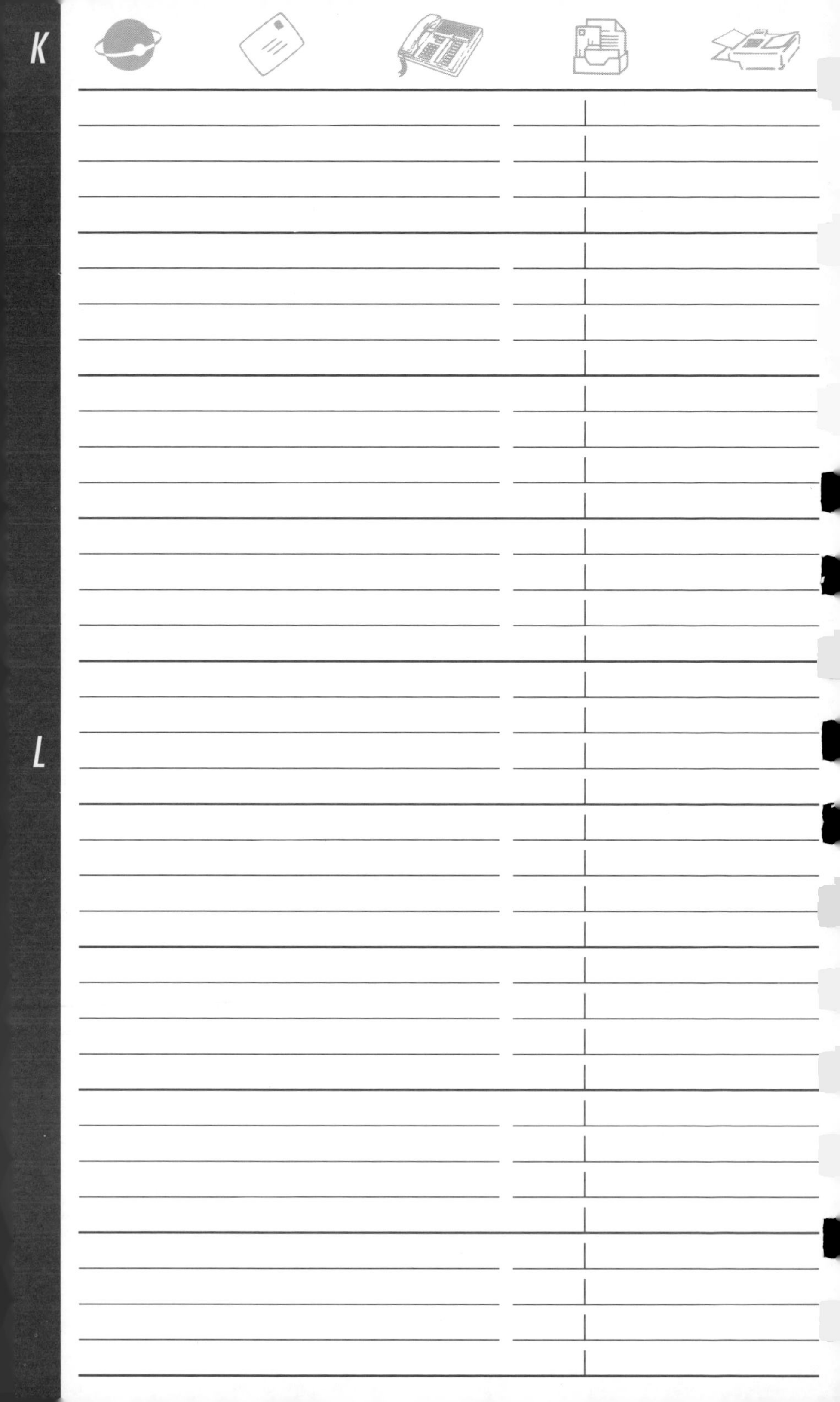
K
L

Mom	408	821-3483

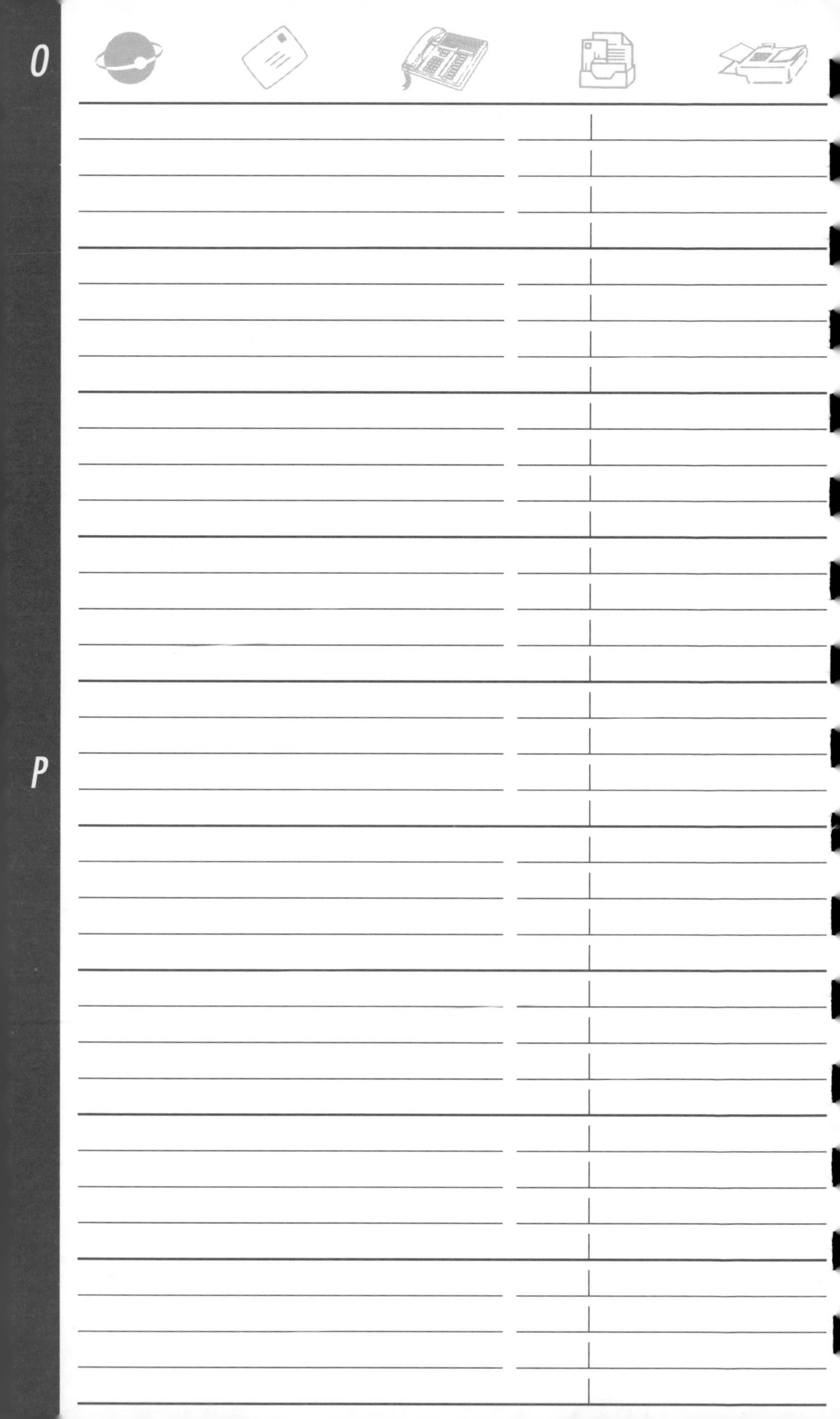
O
P

Q
R

S

Steven Thanh	408	9450538

T

Thi Tran	408	719-1815

U

Vivian Nguyen 408 | 946-5947

V

W
X

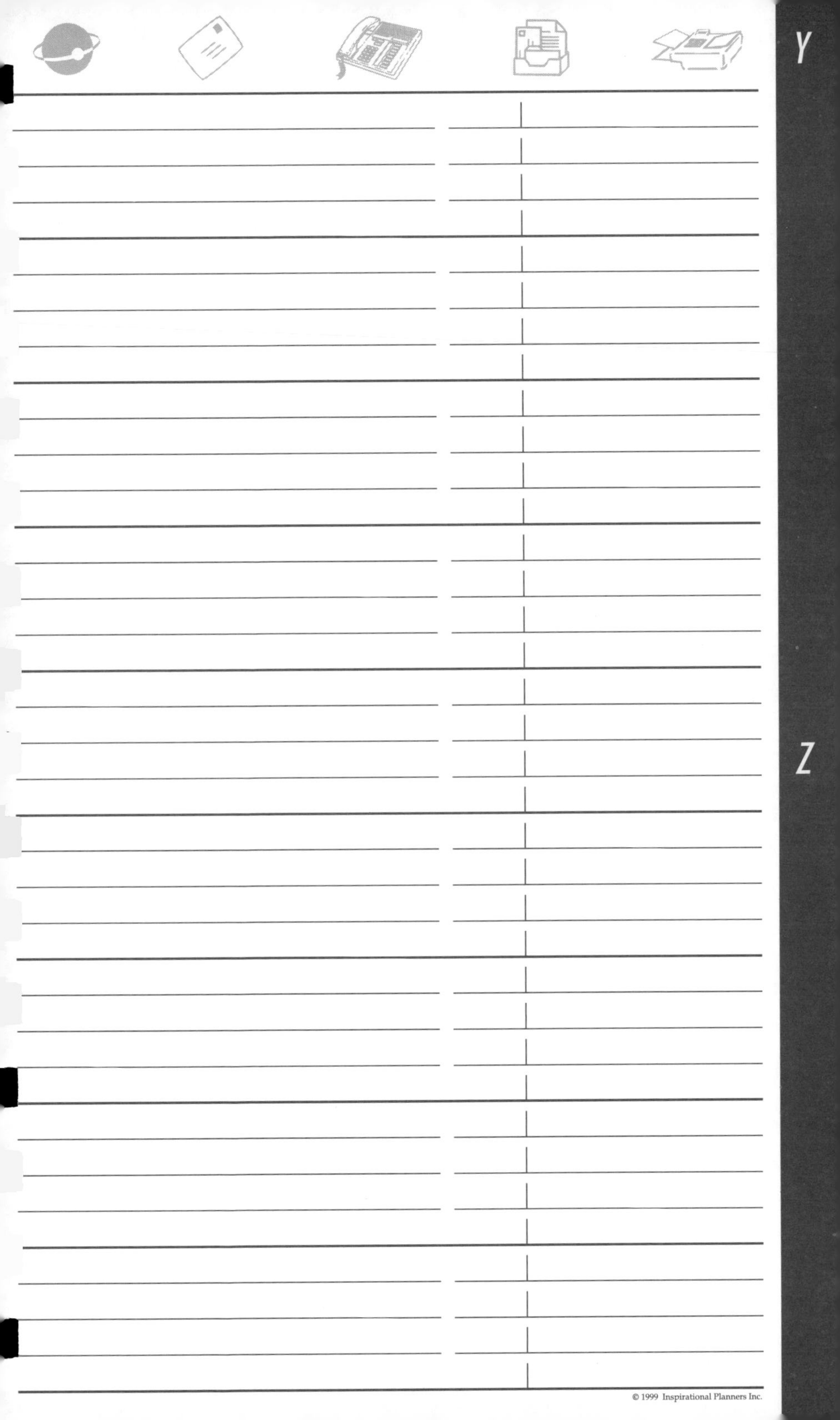
Y
Z

Frequently Called Numbers

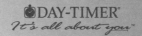

In the spirit of supporting people in need, and in keeping with the traditions of giving that the publisher and co-authors of Chicken Soup For The Soul® established, Inspirational Planners Incorporated and Day-Timer Inc. will be donating a portion of the profit from every organizer sold to one of the following organizations:

Save the Children Federation

For over 65 years Save the Children, a nonprofit organization, has been committed to making positive changes in the lives of disadvantaged children throughout the world. By providing access to caring adults, structured and secure after school activities, along with numerous other health, educational and emergency relief programs, Save the Children has made a world of difference in over 40 nations.

Soup Kitchens for the Soul

Soup Kitchens for the Soul donates Chicken Soup for the Soul books to individuals and organizations that cannot afford to purchase them. Books are given to homeless and battered women shelters, schools, hospitals and churches (to name a few). Over 15,000 books have already been donated! Organizers will also be donated.

Breast Cancer Research Foundation

This nonprofit organization is dedicated to funding leading-edge clinical research into the causes and treatment of breast cancer. Through its continued support of outstanding medical institutions across North America, the Foundation is able to help combat this deadly disease.

Yellow Ribbon Project

The main objective of the Yellow Ribbon Project is to help prevent teen suicides. Documented evidence shows that the Yellow Ribbon Project has saved the lives of over 1,000 teens. This nonprofit organization also encourages individuals to become involved by helping to set up local chapters of the Yellow Ribbon Project in their own communities.

Dyslexia Awareness and Resource Centre

A large percentage of juveniles in prisons and detention centers are dyslexic. This organization helps those who are dyslexic by teaching them to read, learn and grow in a way that is conducive to their disability.

Alley Cat Allies

Alley Cat Allies (ACA), the National Feral Cat Network, is a clearinghouse for information on non-lethal feral cat population control. Feral cats are domestic cats that have reverted to a wild state. ACA offers guidelines on the proper procedures of managing feral cat colonies, conducts regional training workshops, and publishes an award-winning quarterly newsletter, *Alley Cat Action*.

ACTIVITY PLANNER

ACTIVITY PLANNER

IT'S NEVER TOO LATE

Several years ago, while attending a communications course, I experienced a most unusual process. The instructor asked us to list anything in our past that we felt ashamed of, guilty about, incomplete about or that we regretted. The next week he invited participants to read their lists aloud. This seemed like a very private process, but there's always some brave soul in the crowd who will volunteer. As people read their lists, mine grew longer. After three weeks, I had 101 items. The instructor then suggested that we find ways to make amends, apologize to people or take some action to right any wrongdoing. I seriously wondered how this could ever improve my communications, and had visions of alienating just about everyone in my life.

The next week, the man next to me raised his hand and volunteered this story:

While making my list, I remembered an incident from high school. I grew up in a small town in Iowa. There was a sheriff in town that none of us kids liked. One night, my two buddies and I decided to play a trick on Sheriff Brown. After drinking a few beers, we found a can of red paint, climbed the tall water tank in the middle of town, and wrote on the tank, in bright red letters: Sheriff Brown is an s.o.b. The next day, the town arose to see our glorious sign. Within two hours, Sheriff Brown had the three of us in his office. My friends confessed and I lied, denying the truth. No one ever found out.

Nearly 20 years later, Sheriff Brown's name appears on my list. I didn't even know if he was still alive. Last weekend, I dialed Information in my hometown back in Iowa. Sure enough, there was a Roger Brown still listed. I dialed his number. After a few rings, I heard: "Hello?" I said: "Sheriff Brown?" Pause. "Yup." "Well, this is Jimmy Calkins. And I want you to know that I did it." Pause. "I knew it!" he yelled back. We had a good laugh and a lively discussion. His closing words were: "Jimmy, I always felt badly for you because your buddies got it off their chests, and I knew you were carrying it around all these years. I want to thank you for calling me . . . for your sake."

Jimmy inspired me to clear up all 101 items on my list. It took me almost two years, but it became the springboard and true inspiration for my career as a conflict mediator. No matter how difficult the conflict, crisis or situation, I always remember that it's never too late to clear up the past and begin resolution.

Marilyn Manning

ACTIVITY PLANNER

"Tonight is a light evening — we've just got baseball, scuba class, violin and archeology."

CONSIDER THIS

Eighteen publishers turned down Richard Bach's 10,000-word story about a soaring seagull, ***Jonathan Livingston Seagull,*** *before Macmillan finally published it in 1970. By 1975 it had sold more than seven million copies in the U.S. alone.*

Jack Canfield & Mark Victor Hansen

Family Holidays

Remember *Tickets, Travel, Insurance, Money Documents*

Date	

Long Weekends & Day Trips

Remember *Maps, Brochures, Tickets, Travel Bag*

Date	

Visitors & Relatives

Remember *Directions, Stock Up Food, Film and Fun*

Date	

Birthdays & Special Events

Remember *Invitations, Gifts, Cakes, Games*

Date	

Activity Planner

TO ______________ FROM ______________

2000

JANUARY

S	M	T	W	T	F	S
						1
2	3	4	5	6	7	8
9	10	11	12	13	14	15
16	17	18	19	20	21	22
23	24	25	26	27	28	29
30	31					

FEBRUARY

S	M	T	W	T	F	S
		1	2	3	4	5
6	7	8	9	10	11	12
13	14	15	16	17	18	19
20	21	22	23	24	25	26
27	28	29				

MARCH

S	M	T	W	T	F	S
			1	2	3	4
5	6	7	8	9	10	11
12	13	14	15	16	17	18
19	20	21	22	23	24	25
26	27	28	29	30	31	

APRIL

S	M	T	W	T	F	S
						1
2	3	4	5	6	7	8
9	10	11	12	13	14	15
16	17	18	19	20	21	22
23	24	25	26	27	28	29
30						

MAY

S	M	T	W	T	F	S
	1	2	3	4	5	6
7	8	9	10	11	12	13
14	15	16	17	18	19	20
21	22	23	24	25	26	27
28	29	30	31			

JUNE

S	M	T	W	T	F	S
				1	2	3
4	5	6	7	8	9	10
11	12	13	14	15	16	17
18	19	20	21	22	23	24
25	26	27	28	29	30	

JULY

S	M	T	W	T	F	S
						1
2	3	4	5	6	7	8
9	10	11	12	13	14	15
16	17	18	19	20	21	22
23	24	25	26	27	28	29
30	31					

AUGUST

S	M	T	W	T	F	S
		1	2	3	4	5
6	7	8	9	10	11	12
13	14	15	16	17	18	19
20	21	22	23	24	25	26
27	28	29	30	31		

SEPTEMBER

S	M	T	W	T	F	S
					1	2
3	4	5	6	7	8	9
10	11	12	13	14	15	16
17	18	19	20	21	22	23
24	25	26	27	28	29	30

OCTOBER

S	M	T	W	T	F	S
1	2	3	4	5	6	7
8	9	10	11	12	13	14
15	16	17	18	19	20	21
22	23	24	25	26	27	28
29	30	31				

NOVEMBER

S	M	T	W	T	F	S
			1	2	3	4
5	6	7	8	9	10	11
12	13	14	15	16	17	18
19	20	21	22	23	24	25
26	27	28	29	30		

DECEMBER

S	M	T	W	T	F	S
					1	2
3	4	5	6	7	8	9
10	11	12	13	14	15	16
17	18	19	20	21	22	23
24	25	26	27	28	29	30
31						

Work Around The Home

Remember *Check you have materials and tools needed*

Date	

School Activities

Remember *Times, Location, Contact Name*

Date	

Other

Remember

Date	

Hobbies & Lessons

Remember *Materials, Practice, Studying*

Date	

Health & Fitness

Remember *Dentist, Annual Check-Ups, Optometrist, Fitness Tests*

Date	

Sports & Teams

Remember *Directions, Drivers, Coaches' Numbers, Times*

Date	

Family Holidays
Remember Tickets, Travel, Insurance, Money Documents

Date

Long Weekends & Day Trips
Remember Maps, Brochures, Tickets, Travel Bag

Date

Visitors & Relatives
Remember Directions, Stock Up Food, Film and Fun

Date

Birthdays & Special Events
Remember Invitations, Gifts, Cakes, Games

Date

Activity Planner
TO ______________ FROM ______________

2000

JANUARY

S	M	T	W	T	F	S
						1
2	3	4	5	6	7	8
9	10	11	12	13	14	15
16	17	18	19	20	21	22
23	24	25	26	27	28	29
30	31					

FEBRUARY

S	M	T	W	T	F	S
		1	2	3	4	5
6	7	8	9	10	11	12
13	14	15	16	17	18	19
20	21	22	23	24	25	26
27	28	29				

MARCH

S	M	T	W	T	F	S
			1	2	3	4
5	6	7	8	9	10	11
12	13	14	15	16	17	18
19	20	21	22	23	24	25
26	27	28	29	30	31	

APRIL

S	M	T	W	T	F	S
						1
2	3	4	5	6	7	8
9	10	11	12	13	14	15
16	17	18	19	20	21	22
23	24	25	26	27	28	29
30						

MAY

S	M	T	W	T	F	S
	1	2	3	4	5	6
7	8	9	10	11	12	13
14	15	16	17	18	19	20
21	22	23	24	25	26	27
28	29	30	31			

JUNE

S	M	T	W	T	F	S
				1	2	3
4	5	6	7	8	9	10
11	12	13	14	15	16	17
18	19	20	21	22	23	24
25	26	27	28	29	30	

JULY

S	M	T	W	T	F	S
						1
2	3	4	5	6	7	8
9	10	11	12	13	14	15
16	17	18	19	20	21	22
23	24	25	26	27	28	29
30	31					

AUGUST

S	M	T	W	T	F	S
		1	2	3	4	5
6	7	8	9	10	11	12
13	14	15	16	17	18	19
20	21	22	23	24	25	26
27	28	29	30	31		

SEPTEMBER

S	M	T	W	T	F	S
					1	2
3	4	5	6	7	8	9
10	11	12	13	14	15	16
17	18	19	20	21	22	23
24	25	26	27	28	29	30

OCTOBER

S	M	T	W	T	F	S
1	2	3	4	5	6	7
8	9	10	11	12	13	14
15	16	17	18	19	20	21
22	23	24	25	26	27	28
29	30	31				

NOVEMBER

S	M	T	W	T	F	S
			1	2	3	4
5	6	7	8	9	10	11
12	13	14	15	16	17	18
19	20	21	22	23	24	25
26	27	28	29	30		

DECEMBER

S	M	T	W	T	F	S
					1	2
3	4	5	6	7	8	9
10	11	12	13	14	15	16
17	18	19	20	21	22	23
24	25	26	27	28	29	30
31						

Work Around The Home
Remember Check you have materials and tools needed

Date

School Activities
Remember Times, Location, Contact Name

Date

Other
Remember

Date

Hobbies & Lessons
Remember Materials, Practice, Studying

Date

Health & Fitness
Remember Dentist, Annual Check-Ups, Optometrist, Fitness Tests

Date

Sports & Teams
Remember Directions, Drivers, Coaches' Numbers, Times

Date

Family Holidays
Remember Tickets, Travel, Insurance, Money Documents

Date

Long Weekends & Day Trips
Remember Maps, Brochures, Tickets, Travel Bag

Date

Visitors & Relatives
Remember Directions, Stock Up Food, Film and Fun

Date

Birthdays & Special Events
Remember Invitations, Gifts, Cakes, Games

Date

Activity Planner
TO ____________ FROM ____________

2000

JANUARY

S	M	T	W	T	F	S
						1
2	3	4	5	6	7	8
9	10	11	12	13	14	15
16	17	18	19	20	21	22
23	24	25	26	27	28	29
30	31					

FEBRUARY

S	M	T	W	T	F	S
		1	2	3	4	5
6	7	8	9	10	11	12
13	14	15	16	17	18	19
20	21	22	23	24	25	26
27	28	29				

MARCH

S	M	T	W	T	F	S
			1	2	3	4
5	6	7	8	9	10	11
12	13	14	15	16	17	18
19	20	21	22	23	24	25
26	27	28	29	30	31	

APRIL

S	M	T	W	T	F	S
						1
2	3	4	5	6	7	8
9	10	11	12	13	14	15
16	17	18	19	20	21	22
23	24	25	26	27	28	29
30						

MAY

S	M	T	W	T	F	S
	1	2	3	4	5	6
7	8	9	10	11	12	13
14	15	16	17	18	19	20
21	22	23	24	25	26	27
28	29	30	31			

JUNE

S	M	T	W	T	F	S
				1	2	3
4	5	6	7	8	9	10
11	12	13	14	15	16	17
18	19	20	21	22	23	24
25	26	27	28	29	30	

JULY

S	M	T	W	T	F	S
						1
2	3	4	5	6	7	8
9	10	11	12	13	14	15
16	17	18	19	20	21	22
23	24	25	26	27	28	29
30	31					

AUGUST

S	M	T	W	T	F	S
		1	2	3	4	5
6	7	8	9	10	11	12
13	14	15	16	17	18	19
20	21	22	23	24	25	26
27	28	29	30	31		

SEPTEMBER

S	M	T	W	T	F	S
					1	2
3	4	5	6	7	8	9
10	11	12	13	14	15	16
17	18	19	20	21	22	23
24	25	26	27	28	29	30

OCTOBER

S	M	T	W	T	F	S
1	2	3	4	5	6	7
8	9	10	11	12	13	14
15	16	17	18	19	20	21
22	23	24	25	26	27	28
29	30	31				

NOVEMBER

S	M	T	W	T	F	S
			1	2	3	4
5	6	7	8	9	10	11
12	13	14	15	16	17	18
19	20	21	22	23	24	25
26	27	28	29	30		

DECEMBER

S	M	T	W	T	F	S
					1	2
3	4	5	6	7	8	9
10	11	12	13	14	15	16
17	18	19	20	21	22	23
24	25	26	27	28	29	30
31						

Work Around The Home
Remember Check you have materials and tools needed

Date

School Activities
Remember Times, Location, Contact Name

Date

Other
Remember

Date

Hobbies & Lessons
Remember Materials, Practice, Studying

Date

Health & Fitness
Remember Dentist, Annual Check-Ups, Optometrist, Fitness Tests

Date

Sports & Teams
Remember Directions, Drivers, Coaches' Numbers, Times

Date

Family Holidays
Remember *Tickets, Travel, Insurance, Money Documents*

Date

Long Weekends & Day Trips
Remember *Maps, Brochures, Tickets, Travel Bag*

Date

Visitors & Relatives
Remember *Directions, Stock Up Food, Film and Fun*

Date

Birthdays & Special Events
Remember *Invitations, Gifts, Cakes, Games*

Date

Activity Planner
TO ________________ FROM ________________

2000

JANUARY

S	M	T	W	T	F	S
						1
2	3	4	5	6	7	8
9	10	11	12	13	14	15
16	17	18	19	20	21	22
23	24	25	26	27	28	29
30	31					

FEBRUARY

S	M	T	W	T	F	S
		1	2	3	4	5
6	7	8	9	10	11	12
13	14	15	16	17	18	19
20	21	22	23	24	25	26
27	28	29				

MARCH

S	M	T	W	T	F	S
			1	2	3	4
5	6	7	8	9	10	11
12	13	14	15	16	17	18
19	20	21	22	23	24	25
26	27	28	29	30	31	

APRIL

S	M	T	W	T	F	S
						1
2	3	4	5	6	7	8
9	10	11	12	13	14	15
16	17	18	19	20	21	22
23	24	25	26	27	28	29
30						

MAY

S	M	T	W	T	F	S
	1	2	3	4	5	6
7	8	9	10	11	12	13
14	15	16	17	18	19	20
21	22	23	24	25	26	27
28	29	30	31			

JUNE

S	M	T	W	T	F	S
				1	2	3
4	5	6	7	8	9	10
11	12	13	14	15	16	17
18	19	20	21	22	23	24
25	26	27	28	29	30	

JULY

S	M	T	W	T	F	S
						1
2	3	4	5	6	7	8
9	10	11	12	13	14	15
16	17	18	19	20	21	22
23	24	25	26	27	28	29
30	31					

AUGUST

S	M	T	W	T	F	S
		1	2	3	4	5
6	7	8	9	10	11	12
13	14	15	16	17	18	19
20	21	22	23	24	25	26
27	28	29	30	31		

SEPTEMBER

S	M	T	W	T	F	S
					1	2
3	4	5	6	7	8	9
10	11	12	13	14	15	16
17	18	19	20	21	22	23
24	25	26	27	28	29	30

OCTOBER

S	M	T	W	T	F	S
1	2	3	4	5	6	7
8	9	10	11	12	13	14
15	16	17	18	19	20	21
22	23	24	25	26	27	28
29	30	31				

NOVEMBER

S	M	T	W	T	F	S
			1	2	3	4
5	6	7	8	9	10	11
12	13	14	15	16	17	18
19	20	21	22	23	24	25
26	27	28	29	30		

DECEMBER

S	M	T	W	T	F	S
					1	2
3	4	5	6	7	8	9
10	11	12	13	14	15	16
17	18	19	20	21	22	23
24	25	26	27	28	29	30
31						

Work Around The Home
Remember *Check you have materials and tools needed*

Date

School Activities
Remember *Times, Location, Contact Name*

Date

Other
Remember

Date

Hobbies & Lessons
Remember *Materials, Practice, Studying*

Date

Health & Fitness
Remember *Dentist, Annual Check-Ups, Optometrist, Fitness Tests*

Date

Sports & Teams
Remember *Directions, Drivers, Coaches' Numbers, Times*

Date

Family Holidays
Remember Tickets, Travel, Insurance, Money Documents

Date

Long Weekends & Day Trips
Remember Maps, Brochures, Tickets, Travel Bag

Date

Visitors & Relatives
Remember Directions, Stock Up Food, Film and Fun

Date

Birthdays & Special Events
Remember Invitations, Gifts, Cakes, Games

Date

Activity Planner
TO ________________ FROM ________________

2000

JANUARY

S	M	T	W	T	F	S
						1
2	3	4	5	6	7	8
9	10	11	12	13	14	15
16	17	18	19	20	21	22
23	24	25	26	27	28	29
30	31					

FEBRUARY

S	M	T	W	T	F	S
		1	2	3	4	5
6	7	8	9	10	11	12
13	14	15	16	17	18	19
20	21	22	23	24	25	26
27	28	29				

MARCH

S	M	T	W	T	F	S
			1	2	3	4
5	6	7	8	9	10	11
12	13	14	15	16	17	18
19	20	21	22	23	24	25
26	27	28	29	30	31	

APRIL

S	M	T	W	T	F	S
						1
2	3	4	5	6	7	8
9	10	11	12	13	14	15
16	17	18	19	20	21	22
23	24	25	26	27	28	29
30						

MAY

S	M	T	W	T	F	S
	1	2	3	4	5	6
7	8	9	10	11	12	13
14	15	16	17	18	19	20
21	22	23	24	25	26	27
28	29	30	31			

JUNE

S	M	T	W	T	F	S
				1	2	3
4	5	6	7	8	9	10
11	12	13	14	15	16	17
18	19	20	21	22	23	24
25	26	27	28	29	30	

JULY

S	M	T	W	T	F	S
						1
2	3	4	5	6	7	8
9	10	11	12	13	14	15
16	17	18	19	20	21	22
23	24	25	26	27	28	29
30	31					

AUGUST

S	M	T	W	T	F	S
		1	2	3	4	5
6	7	8	9	10	11	12
13	14	15	16	17	18	19
20	21	22	23	24	25	26
27	28	29	30	31		

SEPTEMBER

S	M	T	W	T	F	S
					1	2
3	4	5	6	7	8	9
10	11	12	13	14	15	16
17	18	19	20	21	22	23
24	25	26	27	28	29	30

OCTOBER

S	M	T	W	T	F	S
1	2	3	4	5	6	7
8	9	10	11	12	13	14
15	16	17	18	19	20	21
22	23	24	25	26	27	28
29	30	31				

NOVEMBER

S	M	T	W	T	F	S
			1	2	3	4
5	6	7	8	9	10	11
12	13	14	15	16	17	18
19	20	21	22	23	24	25
26	27	28	29	30		

DECEMBER

S	M	T	W	T	F	S
					1	2
3	4	5	6	7	8	9
10	11	12	13	14	15	16
17	18	19	20	21	22	23
24	25	26	27	28	29	30
31						

Work Around The Home
Remember Check you have materials and tools needed

Date

School Activities
Remember Times, Location, Contact Name

Date

Other
Remember

Date

Hobbies & Lessons
Remember Materials, Practice, Studying

Date

Health & Fitness
Remember Dentist, Annual Check-Ups, Optometrist, Fitness Tests

Date

Sports & Teams
Remember Directions, Drivers, Coaches' Numbers, Times

Date

Family Holidays

Remember Tickets, Travel, Insurance, Money Documents

Date

Long Weekends & Day Trips

Remember Maps, Brochures, Tickets, Travel Bag

Date

Visitors & Relatives

Remember Directions, Stock Up Food, Film and Fun

Date

Birthdays & Special Events

Remember Invitations, Gifts, Cakes, Games

Date

Activity Planner

TO ________________ FROM ________________

2000

JANUARY

S	M	T	W	T	F	S
						1
2	3	4	5	6	7	8
9	10	11	12	13	14	15
16	17	18	19	20	21	22
23	24	25	26	27	28	29
30	31					

FEBRUARY

S	M	T	W	T	F	S
		1	2	3	4	5
6	7	8	9	10	11	12
13	14	15	16	17	18	19
20	21	22	23	24	25	26
27	28	29				

MARCH

S	M	T	W	T	F	S
			1	2	3	4
5	6	7	8	9	10	11
12	13	14	15	16	17	18
19	20	21	22	23	24	25
26	27	28	29	30	31	

APRIL

S	M	T	W	T	F	S
						1
2	3	4	5	6	7	8
9	10	11	12	13	14	15
16	17	18	19	20	21	22
23	24	25	26	27	28	29
30						

MAY

S	M	T	W	T	F	S
	1	2	3	4	5	6
7	8	9	10	11	12	13
14	15	16	17	18	19	20
21	22	23	24	25	26	27
28	29	30	31			

JUNE

S	M	T	W	T	F	S
				1	2	3
4	5	6	7	8	9	10
11	12	13	14	15	16	17
18	19	20	21	22	23	24
25	26	27	28	29	30	

JULY

S	M	T	W	T	F	S
						1
2	3	4	5	6	7	8
9	10	11	12	13	14	15
16	17	18	19	20	21	22
23	24	25	26	27	28	29
30	31					

AUGUST

S	M	T	W	T	F	S
		1	2	3	4	5
6	7	8	9	10	11	12
13	14	15	16	17	18	19
20	21	22	23	24	25	26
27	28	29	30	31		

SEPTEMBER

S	M	T	W	T	F	S
					1	2
3	4	5	6	7	8	9
10	11	12	13	14	15	16
17	18	19	20	21	22	23
24	25	26	27	28	29	30

OCTOBER

S	M	T	W	T	F	S
1	2	3	4	5	6	7
8	9	10	11	12	13	14
15	16	17	18	19	20	21
22	23	24	25	26	27	28
29	30	31				

NOVEMBER

S	M	T	W	T	F	S
			1	2	3	4
5	6	7	8	9	10	11
12	13	14	15	16	17	18
19	20	21	22	23	24	25
26	27	28	29	30		

DECEMBER

S	M	T	W	T	F	S
					1	2
3	4	5	6	7	8	9
10	11	12	13	14	15	16
17	18	19	20	21	22	23
24	25	26	27	28	29	30
31						

Work Around The Home

Remember Check you have materials and tools needed

Date

School Activities

Remember Times, Location, Contact Name

Date

Other

Remember

Date

Hobbies & Lessons

Remember Materials, Practice, Studying

Date

Health & Fitness

Remember Dentist, Annual Check-Ups, Optometrist, Fitness Tests

Date

Sports & Teams

Remember Directions, Drivers, Coaches' Numbers, Times

Date

Family Holidays
Remember Tickets, Travel, Insurance, Money Documents

Date

Long Weekends & Day Trips
Remember Maps, Brochures, Tickets, Travel Bag

Date

Visitors & Relatives
Remember Directions, Stock Up Food, Film and Fun

Date

Birthdays & Special Events
Remember Invitations, Gifts, Cakes, Games

Date

Activity Planner
TO ________________ FROM ________________

2000

JANUARY

S	M	T	W	T	F	S
						1
2	3	4	5	6	7	8
9	10	11	12	13	14	15
16	17	18	19	20	21	22
23	24	25	26	27	28	29
30	31					

FEBRUARY

S	M	T	W	T	F	S
		1	2	3	4	5
6	7	8	9	10	11	12
13	14	15	16	17	18	19
20	21	22	23	24	25	26
27	28	29				

MARCH

S	M	T	W	T	F	S
			1	2	3	4
5	6	7	8	9	10	11
12	13	14	15	16	17	18
19	20	21	22	23	24	25
26	27	28	29	30	31	

APRIL

S	M	T	W	T	F	S
						1
2	3	4	5	6	7	8
9	10	11	12	13	14	15
16	17	18	19	20	21	22
23	24	25	26	27	28	29
30						

MAY

S	M	T	W	T	F	S
	1	2	3	4	5	6
7	8	9	10	11	12	13
14	15	16	17	18	19	20
21	22	23	24	25	26	27
28	29	30	31			

JUNE

S	M	T	W	T	F	S
				1	2	3
4	5	6	7	8	9	10
11	12	13	14	15	16	17
18	19	20	21	22	23	24
25	26	27	28	29	30	

JULY

S	M	T	W	T	F	S
						1
2	3	4	5	6	7	8
9	10	11	12	13	14	15
16	17	18	19	20	21	22
23	24	25	26	27	28	29
30	31					

AUGUST

S	M	T	W	T	F	S
		1	2	3	4	5
6	7	8	9	10	11	12
13	14	15	16	17	18	19
20	21	22	23	24	25	26
27	28	29	30	31		

SEPTEMBER

S	M	T	W	T	F	S
					1	2
3	4	5	6	7	8	9
10	11	12	13	14	15	16
17	18	19	20	21	22	23
24	25	26	27	28	29	30

OCTOBER

S	M	T	W	T	F	S
1	2	3	4	5	6	7
8	9	10	11	12	13	14
15	16	17	18	19	20	21
22	23	24	25	26	27	28
29	30	31				

NOVEMBER

S	M	T	W	T	F	S
			1	2	3	4
5	6	7	8	9	10	11
12	13	14	15	16	17	18
19	20	21	22	23	24	25
26	27	28	29	30		

DECEMBER

S	M	T	W	T	F	S
					1	2
3	4	5	6	7	8	9
10	11	12	13	14	15	16
17	18	19	20	21	22	23
24	25	26	27	28	29	30
31						

Work Around The Home
Remember Check you have materials and tools needed

Date

School Activities
Remember Times, Location, Contact Name

Date

Other
Remember

Date

Hobbies & Lessons
Remember Materials, Practice, Studying

Date

Health & Fitness
Remember Dentist, Annual Check-Ups, Optometrist, Fitness Tests

Date

Sports & Teams
Remember Directions, Drivers, Coaches' Numbers, Times

Date

Family Holidays

Remember Tickets, Travel, Insurance, Money Documents

Date	

Long Weekends & Day Trips

Remember Maps, Brochures, Tickets, Travel Bag

Date	

Visitors & Relatives

Remember Directions, Stock Up Food, Film and Fun

Date	

Birthdays & Special Events

Remember Invitations, Gifts, Cakes, Games

Date	

Activity Planner

TO ______________ FROM ______________

2000

JANUARY

S	M	T	W	T	F	S
						1
2	3	4	5	6	7	8
9	10	11	12	13	14	15
16	17	18	19	20	21	22
23	24	25	26	27	28	29
30	31					

FEBRUARY

S	M	T	W	T	F	S
		1	2	3	4	5
6	7	8	9	10	11	12
13	14	15	16	17	18	19
20	21	22	23	24	25	26
27	28	29				

MARCH

S	M	T	W	T	F	S
			1	2	3	4
5	6	7	8	9	10	11
12	13	14	15	16	17	18
19	20	21	22	23	24	25
26	27	28	29	30	31	

APRIL

S	M	T	W	T	F	S
						1
2	3	4	5	6	7	8
9	10	11	12	13	14	15
16	17	18	19	20	21	22
23	24	25	26	27	28	29
30						

MAY

S	M	T	W	T	F	S
	1	2	3	4	5	6
7	8	9	10	11	12	13
14	15	16	17	18	19	20
21	22	23	24	25	26	27
28	29	30	31			

JUNE

S	M	T	W	T	F	S
				1	2	3
4	5	6	7	8	9	10
11	12	13	14	15	16	17
18	19	20	21	22	23	24
25	26	27	28	29	30	

JULY

S	M	T	W	T	F	S
						1
2	3	4	5	6	7	8
9	10	11	12	13	14	15
16	17	18	19	20	21	22
23	24	25	26	27	28	29
30	31					

AUGUST

S	M	T	W	T	F	S
		1	2	3	4	5
6	7	8	9	10	11	12
13	14	15	16	17	18	19
20	21	22	23	24	25	26
27	28	29	30	31		

SEPTEMBER

S	M	T	W	T	F	S
					1	2
3	4	5	6	7	8	9
10	11	12	13	14	15	16
17	18	19	20	21	22	23
24	25	26	27	28	29	30

OCTOBER

S	M	T	W	T	F	S
1	2	3	4	5	6	7
8	9	10	11	12	13	14
15	16	17	18	19	20	21
22	23	24	25	26	27	28
29	30	31				

NOVEMBER

S	M	T	W	T	F	S
			1	2	3	4
5	6	7	8	9	10	11
12	13	14	15	16	17	18
19	20	21	22	23	24	25
26	27	28	29	30		

DECEMBER

S	M	T	W	T	F	S
					1	2
3	4	5	6	7	8	9
10	11	12	13	14	15	16
17	18	19	20	21	22	23
24	25	26	27	28	29	30
31						

Work Around The Home

Remember Check you have materials and tools needed

Date	

School Activities

Remember Times, Location, Contact Name

Date	

Other

Remember

Date	

Hobbies & Lessons

Remember Materials, Practice, Studying

Date	

Health & Fitness

Remember Dentist, Annual Check-Ups, Optometrist, Fitness Tests

Date	

Sports & Teams

Remember Directions, Drivers, Coaches' Numbers, Times

Date	

Family Holidays
Remember Tickets, Travel, Insurance, Money Documents

Date

Long Weekends & Day Trips
Remember Maps, Brochures, Tickets, Travel Bag

Date

Visitors & Relatives
Remember Directions, Stock Up Food, Film and Fun

Date

Birthdays & Special Events
Remember Invitations, Gifts, Cakes, Games

Date

Activity Planner
TO ________________ FROM ________________

2000

JANUARY

S	M	T	W	T	F	S
						1
2	3	4	5	6	7	8
9	10	11	12	13	14	15
16	17	18	19	20	21	22
23	24	25	26	27	28	29
30	31					

FEBRUARY

S	M	T	W	T	F	S
		1	2	3	4	5
6	7	8	9	10	11	12
13	14	15	16	17	18	19
20	21	22	23	24	25	26
27	28	29				

MARCH

S	M	T	W	T	F	S
			1	2	3	4
5	6	7	8	9	10	11
12	13	14	15	16	17	18
19	20	21	22	23	24	25
26	27	28	29	30	31	

APRIL

S	M	T	W	T	F	S
						1
2	3	4	5	6	7	8
9	10	11	12	13	14	15
16	17	18	19	20	21	22
23	24	25	26	27	28	29
30						

MAY

S	M	T	W	T	F	S
	1	2	3	4	5	6
7	8	9	10	11	12	13
14	15	16	17	18	19	20
21	22	23	24	25	26	27
28	29	30	31			

JUNE

S	M	T	W	T	F	S
				1	2	3
4	5	6	7	8	9	10
11	12	13	14	15	16	17
18	19	20	21	22	23	24
25	26	27	28	29	30	

JULY

S	M	T	W	T	F	S
						1
2	3	4	5	6	7	8
9	10	11	12	13	14	15
16	17	18	19	20	21	22
23	24	25	26	27	28	29
30	31					

AUGUST

S	M	T	W	T	F	S
		1	2	3	4	5
6	7	8	9	10	11	12
13	14	15	16	17	18	19
20	21	22	23	24	25	26
27	28	29	30	31		

SEPTEMBER

S	M	T	W	T	F	S
					1	2
3	4	5	6	7	8	9
10	11	12	13	14	15	16
17	18	19	20	21	22	23
24	25	26	27	28	29	30

OCTOBER

S	M	T	W	T	F	S
1	2	3	4	5	6	7
8	9	10	11	12	13	14
15	16	17	18	19	20	21
22	23	24	25	26	27	28
29	30	31				

NOVEMBER

S	M	T	W	T	F	S
			1	2	3	4
5	6	7	8	9	10	11
12	13	14	15	16	17	18
19	20	21	22	23	24	25
26	27	28	29	30		

DECEMBER

S	M	T	W	T	F	S
					1	2
3	4	5	6	7	8	9
10	11	12	13	14	15	16
17	18	19	20	21	22	23
24	25	26	27	28	29	30
31						

Work Around The Home
Remember Check you have materials and tools needed

Date

School Activities
Remember Times, Location, Contact Name

Date

Other
Remember

Date

Hobbies & Lessons
Remember Materials, Practice, Studying

Date

Health & Fitness
Remember Dentist, Annual Check-Ups, Optometrist, Fitness Tests

Date

Sports & Teams
Remember Directions, Drivers, Coaches' Numbers, Times

Date

Family Holidays

Remember Tickets, Travel, Insurance, Money Documents

Date

Long Weekends & Day Trips

Remember Maps, Brochures, Tickets, Travel Bag

Date

Visitors & Relatives

Remember Directions, Stock Up Food, Film and Fun

Date

Birthdays & Special Events

Remember Invitations, Gifts, Cakes, Games

Date

Activity Planner

TO ________________ FROM ________________

2000

JANUARY

S	M	T	W	T	F	S
						1
2	3	4	5	6	7	8
9	10	11	12	13	14	15
16	17	18	19	20	21	22
23	24	25	26	27	28	29
30	31					

FEBRUARY

S	M	T	W	T	F	S
		1	2	3	4	5
6	7	8	9	10	11	12
13	14	15	16	17	18	19
20	21	22	23	24	25	26
27	28	29				

MARCH

S	M	T	W	T	F	S
			1	2	3	4
5	6	7	8	9	10	11
12	13	14	15	16	17	18
19	20	21	22	23	24	25
26	27	28	29	30	31	

APRIL

S	M	T	W	T	F	S
						1
2	3	4	5	6	7	8
9	10	11	12	13	14	15
16	17	18	19	20	21	22
23	24	25	26	27	28	29
30						

MAY

S	M	T	W	T	F	S
	1	2	3	4	5	6
7	8	9	10	11	12	13
14	15	16	17	18	19	20
21	22	23	24	25	26	27
28	29	30	31			

JUNE

S	M	T	W	T	F	S
				1	2	3
4	5	6	7	8	9	10
11	12	13	14	15	16	17
18	19	20	21	22	23	24
25	26	27	28	29	30	

JULY

S	M	T	W	T	F	S
						1
2	3	4	5	6	7	8
9	10	11	12	13	14	15
16	17	18	19	20	21	22
23	24	25	26	27	28	29
30	31					

AUGUST

S	M	T	W	T	F	S
		1	2	3	4	5
6	7	8	9	10	11	12
13	14	15	16	17	18	19
20	21	22	23	24	25	26
27	28	29	30	31		

SEPTEMBER

S	M	T	W	T	F	S
					1	2
3	4	5	6	7	8	9
10	11	12	13	14	15	16
17	18	19	20	21	22	23
24	25	26	27	28	29	30

OCTOBER

S	M	T	W	T	F	S
1	2	3	4	5	6	7
8	9	10	11	12	13	14
15	16	17	18	19	20	21
22	23	24	25	26	27	28
29	30	31				

NOVEMBER

S	M	T	W	T	F	S
			1	2	3	4
5	6	7	8	9	10	11
12	13	14	15	16	17	18
19	20	21	22	23	24	25
26	27	28	29	30		

DECEMBER

S	M	T	W	T	F	S
					1	2
3	4	5	6	7	8	9
10	11	12	13	14	15	16
17	18	19	20	21	22	23
24	25	26	27	28	29	30
31						

Work Around The Home

Remember Check you have materials and tools needed

Date

School Activities

Remember Times, Location, Contact Name

Date

Other

Remember

Date

Hobbies & Lessons

Remember Materials, Practice, Studying

Date

Health & Fitness

Remember Dentist, Annual Check-Ups, Optometrist, Fitness Tests

Date

Sports & Teams

Remember Directions, Drivers, Coaches' Numbers, Times

Date

Family Holidays

Remember Tickets, Travel, Insurance, Money Documents

Date

Long Weekends & Day Trips

Remember Maps, Brochures, Tickets, Travel Bag

Date

Visitors & Relatives

Remember Directions, Stock Up Food, Film and Fun

Date

Birthdays & Special Events

Remember Invitations, Gifts, Cakes, Games

Date

Activity Planner

TO ______________ FROM ______________

2000

JANUARY

S	M	T	W	T	F	S
						1
2	3	4	5	6	7	8
9	10	11	12	13	14	15
16	17	18	19	20	21	22
23	24	25	26	27	28	29
30	31					

FEBRUARY

S	M	T	W	T	F	S
		1	2	3	4	5
6	7	8	9	10	11	12
13	14	15	16	17	18	19
20	21	22	23	24	25	26
27	28	29				

MARCH

S	M	T	W	T	F	S
			1	2	3	4
5	6	7	8	9	10	11
12	13	14	15	16	17	18
19	20	21	22	23	24	25
26	27	28	29	30	31	

APRIL

S	M	T	W	T	F	S
						1
2	3	4	5	6	7	8
9	10	11	12	13	14	15
16	17	18	19	20	21	22
23	24	25	26	27	28	29
30						

MAY

S	M	T	W	T	F	S
	1	2	3	4	5	6
7	8	9	10	11	12	13
14	15	16	17	18	19	20
21	22	23	24	25	26	27
28	29	30	31			

JUNE

S	M	T	W	T	F	S
				1	2	3
4	5	6	7	8	9	10
11	12	13	14	15	16	17
18	19	20	21	22	23	24
25	26	27	28	29	30	

JULY

S	M	T	W	T	F	S
						1
2	3	4	5	6	7	8
9	10	11	12	13	14	15
16	17	18	19	20	21	22
23	24	25	26	27	28	29
30	31					

AUGUST

S	M	T	W	T	F	S
		1	2	3	4	5
6	7	8	9	10	11	12
13	14	15	16	17	18	19
20	21	22	23	24	25	26
27	28	29	30	31		

SEPTEMBER

S	M	T	W	T	F	S
					1	2
3	4	5	6	7	8	9
10	11	12	13	14	15	16
17	18	19	20	21	22	23
24	25	26	27	28	29	30

OCTOBER

S	M	T	W	T	F	S
1	2	3	4	5	6	7
8	9	10	11	12	13	14
15	16	17	18	19	20	21
22	23	24	25	26	27	28
29	30	31				

NOVEMBER

S	M	T	W	T	F	S
			1	2	3	4
5	6	7	8	9	10	11
12	13	14	15	16	17	18
19	20	21	22	23	24	25
26	27	28	29	30		

DECEMBER

S	M	T	W	T	F	S
					1	2
3	4	5	6	7	8	9
10	11	12	13	14	15	16
17	18	19	20	21	22	23
24	25	26	27	28	29	30
31						

Work Around The Home

Remember Check you have materials and tools needed

Date

School Activities

Remember Times, Location, Contact Name

Date

Other

Remember

Date

Hobbies & Lessons

Remember Materials, Practice, Studying

Date

Health & Fitness

Remember Dentist, Annual Check-Ups, Optometrist, Fitness Tests

Date

Sports & Teams

Remember Directions, Drivers, Coaches' Numbers, Times

Date

Family Holidays

Remember Tickets, Travel, Insurance, Money Documents

Date

Long Weekends & Day Trips

Remember Maps, Brochures, Tickets, Travel Bag

Date

Visitors & Relatives

Remember Directions, Stock Up Food, Film and Fun

Date

Birthdays & Special Events

Remember Invitations, Gifts, Cakes, Games

Date

Activity Planner

TO ________________ FROM ________________

2000

JANUARY

S	M	T	W	T	F	S
						1
2	3	4	5	6	7	8
9	10	11	12	13	14	15
16	17	18	19	20	21	22
23	24	25	26	27	28	29
30	31					

FEBRUARY

S	M	T	W	T	F	S
		1	2	3	4	5
6	7	8	9	10	11	12
13	14	15	16	17	18	19
20	21	22	23	24	25	26
27	28	29				

MARCH

S	M	T	W	T	F	S
			1	2	3	4
5	6	7	8	9	10	11
12	13	14	15	16	17	18
19	20	21	22	23	24	25
26	27	28	29	30	31	

APRIL

S	M	T	W	T	F	S
						1
2	3	4	5	6	7	8
9	10	11	12	13	14	15
16	17	18	19	20	21	22
23	24	25	26	27	28	29
30						

MAY

S	M	T	W	T	F	S
	1	2	3	4	5	6
7	8	9	10	11	12	13
14	15	16	17	18	19	20
21	22	23	24	25	26	27
28	29	30	31			

JUNE

S	M	T	W	T	F	S
				1	2	3
4	5	6	7	8	9	10
11	12	13	14	15	16	17
18	19	20	21	22	23	24
25	26	27	28	29	30	

JULY

S	M	T	W	T	F	S
						1
2	3	4	5	6	7	8
9	10	11	12	13	14	15
16	17	18	19	20	21	22
23	24	25	26	27	28	29
30	31					

AUGUST

S	M	T	W	T	F	S
		1	2	3	4	5
6	7	8	9	10	11	12
13	14	15	16	17	18	19
20	21	22	23	24	25	26
27	28	29	30	31		

SEPTEMBER

S	M	T	W	T	F	S
					1	2
3	4	5	6	7	8	9
10	11	12	13	14	15	16
17	18	19	20	21	22	23
24	25	26	27	28	29	30

OCTOBER

S	M	T	W	T	F	S
1	2	3	4	5	6	7
8	9	10	11	12	13	14
15	16	17	18	19	20	21
22	23	24	25	26	27	28
29	30	31				

NOVEMBER

S	M	T	W	T	F	S
			1	2	3	4
5	6	7	8	9	10	11
12	13	14	15	16	17	18
19	20	21	22	23	24	25
26	27	28	29	30		

DECEMBER

S	M	T	W	T	F	S
					1	2
3	4	5	6	7	8	9
10	11	12	13	14	15	16
17	18	19	20	21	22	23
24	25	26	27	28	29	30
31						

Work Around The Home

Remember Check you have materials and tools needed

Date

School Activities

Remember Times, Location, Contact Name

Date

Other

Remember ________________

Date

Hobbies & Lessons

Remember Materials, Practice, Studying

Date

Health & Fitness

Remember Dentist, Annual Check-Ups, Optometrist, Fitness Tests

Date

Sports & Teams

Remember Directions, Drivers, Coaches' Numbers, Times

Date

Family Holidays

Remember *Tickets, Travel, Insurance, Money Documents*

Date

Long Weekends & Day Trips

Remember *Maps, Brochures, Tickets, Travel Bag*

Date

Visitors & Relatives

Remember *Directions, Stock Up Food, Film and Fun*

Date

Birthdays & Special Events

Remember *Invitations, Gifts, Cakes, Games*

Date

Activity Planner

TO ______________ FROM______________

2000

JANUARY

S	M	T	W	T	F	S
						1
2	3	4	5	6	7	8
9	10	11	12	13	14	15
16	17	18	19	20	21	22
23	24	25	26	27	28	29
30	31					

FEBRUARY

S	M	T	W	T	F	S
		1	2	3	4	5
6	7	8	9	10	11	12
13	14	15	16	17	18	19
20	21	22	23	24	25	26
27	28	29				

MARCH

S	M	T	W	T	F	S
			1	2	3	4
5	6	7	8	9	10	11
12	13	14	15	16	17	18
19	20	21	22	23	24	25
26	27	28	29	30	31	

APRIL

S	M	T	W	T	F	S
						1
2	3	4	5	6	7	8
9	10	11	12	13	14	15
16	17	18	19	20	21	22
23	24	25	26	27	28	29
30						

MAY

S	M	T	W	T	F	S
	1	2	3	4	5	6
7	8	9	10	11	12	13
14	15	16	17	18	19	20
21	22	23	24	25	26	27
28	29	30	31			

JUNE

S	M	T	W	T	F	S
				1	2	3
4	5	6	7	8	9	10
11	12	13	14	15	16	17
18	19	20	21	22	23	24
25	26	27	28	29	30	

JULY

S	M	T	W	T	F	S
						1
2	3	4	5	6	7	8
9	10	11	12	13	14	15
16	17	18	19	20	21	22
23	24	25	26	27	28	29
30	31					

AUGUST

S	M	T	W	T	F	S
		1	2	3	4	5
6	7	8	9	10	11	12
13	14	15	16	17	18	19
20	21	22	23	24	25	26
27	28	29	30	31		

SEPTEMBER

S	M	T	W	T	F	S
					1	2
3	4	5	6	7	8	9
10	11	12	13	14	15	16
17	18	19	20	21	22	23
24	25	26	27	28	29	30

OCTOBER

S	M	T	W	T	F	S
1	2	3	4	5	6	7
8	9	10	11	12	13	14
15	16	17	18	19	20	21
22	23	24	25	26	27	28
29	30	31				

NOVEMBER

S	M	T	W	T	F	S
			1	2	3	4
5	6	7	8	9	10	11
12	13	14	15	16	17	18
19	20	21	22	23	24	25
26	27	28	29	30		

DECEMBER

S	M	T	W	T	F	S
					1	2
3	4	5	6	7	8	9
10	11	12	13	14	15	16
17	18	19	20	21	22	23
24	25	26	27	28	29	30
31						

Work Around The Home

Remember *Check you have materials and tools needed*

Date

School Activities

Remember *Times, Location, Contact Name*

Date

Other

Remember

Date

Hobbies & Lessons

Remember *Materials, Practice, Studying*

Date

Health & Fitness

Remember *Dentist, Annual Check-Ups, Optometrist, Fitness Tests*

Date

Sports & Teams

Remember *Directions, Drivers, Coaches' Numbers, Times*

Date

Family Holidays

Remember *Tickets, Travel, Insurance, Money Documents*

Date

Long Weekends & Day Trips

Remember *Maps, Brochures, Tickets, Travel Bag*

Date

Visitors & Relatives

Remember *Directions, Stock Up Food, Film and Fun*

Date

Birthdays & Special Events

Remember *Invitations, Gifts, Cakes, Games*

Date

Activity Planner

TO ________________ FROM ________________

2000

JANUARY

S	M	T	W	T	F	S
						1
2	3	4	5	6	7	8
9	10	11	12	13	14	15
16	17	18	19	20	21	22
23	24	25	26	27	28	29
30	31					

FEBRUARY

S	M	T	W	T	F	S
		1	2	3	4	5
6	7	8	9	10	11	12
13	14	15	16	17	18	19
20	21	22	23	24	25	26
27	28	29				

MARCH

S	M	T	W	T	F	S
			1	2	3	4
5	6	7	8	9	10	11
12	13	14	15	16	17	18
19	20	21	22	23	24	25
26	27	28	29	30	31	

APRIL

S	M	T	W	T	F	S
						1
2	3	4	5	6	7	8
9	10	11	12	13	14	15
16	17	18	19	20	21	22
23	24	25	26	27	28	29
30						

MAY

S	M	T	W	T	F	S
	1	2	3	4	5	6
7	8	9	10	11	12	13
14	15	16	17	18	19	20
21	22	23	24	25	26	27
28	29	30	31			

JUNE

S	M	T	W	T	F	S
				1	2	3
4	5	6	7	8	9	10
11	12	13	14	15	16	17
18	19	20	21	22	23	24
25	26	27	28	29	30	

JULY

S	M	T	W	T	F	S
						1
2	3	4	5	6	7	8
9	10	11	12	13	14	15
16	17	18	19	20	21	22
23	24	25	26	27	28	29
30	31					

AUGUST

S	M	T	W	T	F	S
		1	2	3	4	5
6	7	8	9	10	11	12
13	14	15	16	17	18	19
20	21	22	23	24	25	26
27	28	29	30	31		

SEPTEMBER

S	M	T	W	T	F	S
					1	2
3	4	5	6	7	8	9
10	11	12	13	14	15	16
17	18	19	20	21	22	23
24	25	26	27	28	29	30

OCTOBER

S	M	T	W	T	F	S
1	2	3	4	5	6	7
8	9	10	11	12	13	14
15	16	17	18	19	20	21
22	23	24	25	26	27	28
29	30	31				

NOVEMBER

S	M	T	W	T	F	S
			1	2	3	4
5	6	7	8	9	10	11
12	13	14	15	16	17	18
19	20	21	22	23	24	25
26	27	28	29	30		

DECEMBER

S	M	T	W	T	F	S
					1	2
3	4	5	6	7	8	9
10	11	12	13	14	15	16
17	18	19	20	21	22	23
24	25	26	27	28	29	30
31						

Work Around The Home

Remember *Check you have materials and tools needed*

Date

School Activities

Remember *Times, Location, Contact Name*

Date

Other

Remember

Date

Hobbies & Lessons

Remember *Materials, Practice, Studying*

Date

Health & Fitness

Remember *Dentist, Annual Check-Ups, Optometrist, Fitness Tests*

Date

Sports & Teams

Remember *Directions, Drivers, Coaches' Numbers, Times*

Date

Family Holidays
Remember *Tickets, Travel, Insurance, Money Documents*

Date

Long Weekends & Day Trips
Remember *Maps, Brochures, Tickets, Travel Bag*

Date

Visitors & Relatives
Remember *Directions, Stock Up Food, Film and Fun*

Date

Birthdays & Special Events
Remember *Invitations, Gifts, Cakes, Games*

Date

Activity Planner
TO ________________ FROM ________________

2000

JANUARY

S	M	T	W	T	F	S
						1
2	3	4	5	6	7	8
9	10	11	12	13	14	15
16	17	18	19	20	21	22
23	24	25	26	27	28	29
30	31					

FEBRUARY

S	M	T	W	T	F	S
		1	2	3	4	5
6	7	8	9	10	11	12
13	14	15	16	17	18	19
20	21	22	23	24	25	26
27	28	29				

MARCH

S	M	T	W	T	F	S
			1	2	3	4
5	6	7	8	9	10	11
12	13	14	15	16	17	18
19	20	21	22	23	24	25
26	27	28	29	30	31	

APRIL

S	M	T	W	T	F	S
						1
2	3	4	5	6	7	8
9	10	11	12	13	14	15
16	17	18	19	20	21	22
23	24	25	26	27	28	29
30						

MAY

S	M	T	W	T	F	S
	1	2	3	4	5	6
7	8	9	10	11	12	13
14	15	16	17	18	19	20
21	22	23	24	25	26	27
28	29	30	31			

JUNE

S	M	T	W	T	F	S
				1	2	3
4	5	6	7	8	9	10
11	12	13	14	15	16	17
18	19	20	21	22	23	24
25	26	27	28	29	30	

JULY

S	M	T	W	T	F	S
						1
2	3	4	5	6	7	8
9	10	11	12	13	14	15
16	17	18	19	20	21	22
23	24	25	26	27	28	29
30	31					

AUGUST

S	M	T	W	T	F	S
		1	2	3	4	5
6	7	8	9	10	11	12
13	14	15	16	17	18	19
20	21	22	23	24	25	26
27	28	29	30	31		

SEPTEMBER

S	M	T	W	T	F	S
					1	2
3	4	5	6	7	8	9
10	11	12	13	14	15	16
17	18	19	20	21	22	23
24	25	26	27	28	29	30

OCTOBER

S	M	T	W	T	F	S
1	2	3	4	5	6	7
8	9	10	11	12	13	14
15	16	17	18	19	20	21
22	23	24	25	26	27	28
29	30	31				

NOVEMBER

S	M	T	W	T	F	S
			1	2	3	4
5	6	7	8	9	10	11
12	13	14	15	16	17	18
19	20	21	22	23	24	25
26	27	28	29	30		

DECEMBER

S	M	T	W	T	F	S
					1	2
3	4	5	6	7	8	9
10	11	12	13	14	15	16
17	18	19	20	21	22	23
24	25	26	27	28	29	30
31						

Work Around The Home
Remember *Check you have materials and tools needed*

Date

School Activities
Remember *Times, Location, Contact Name*

Date

Other
Remember

Date

Hobbies & Lessons
Remember *Materials, Practice, Studying*

Date

Health & Fitness
Remember *Dentist, Annual Check-Ups, Optometrist, Fitness Tests*

Date

Sports & Teams
Remember *Directions, Drivers, Coaches' Numbers, Times*

Date

Family Holidays

Remember *Tickets, Travel, Insurance, Money Documents*

Date

Long Weekends & Day Trips

Remember *Maps, Brochures, Tickets, Travel Bag*

Date

Visitors & Relatives

Remember *Directions, Stock Up Food, Film and Fun*

Date

Birthdays & Special Events

Remember *Invitations, Gifts, Cakes, Games*

Date

Activity Planner

TO ________________ FROM ________________

2000

JANUARY

S	M	T	W	T	F	S
						1
2	3	4	5	6	7	8
9	10	11	12	13	14	15
16	17	18	19	20	21	22
23	24	25	26	27	28	29
30	31					

FEBRUARY

S	M	T	W	T	F	S
		1	2	3	4	5
6	7	8	9	10	11	12
13	14	15	16	17	18	19
20	21	22	23	24	25	26
27	28	29				

MARCH

S	M	T	W	T	F	S
			1	2	3	4
5	6	7	8	9	10	11
12	13	14	15	16	17	18
19	20	21	22	23	24	25
26	27	28	29	30	31	

APRIL

S	M	T	W	T	F	S
						1
2	3	4	5	6	7	8
9	10	11	12	13	14	15
16	17	18	19	20	21	22
23	24	25	26	27	28	29
30						

MAY

S	M	T	W	T	F	S
	1	2	3	4	5	6
7	8	9	10	11	12	13
14	15	16	17	18	19	20
21	22	23	24	25	26	27
28	29	30	31			

JUNE

S	M	T	W	T	F	S
				1	2	3
4	5	6	7	8	9	10
11	12	13	14	15	16	17
18	19	20	21	22	23	24
25	26	27	28	29	30	

JULY

S	M	T	W	T	F	S
						1
2	3	4	5	6	7	8
9	10	11	12	13	14	15
16	17	18	19	20	21	22
23	24	25	26	27	28	29
30	31					

AUGUST

S	M	T	W	T	F	S
		1	2	3	4	5
6	7	8	9	10	11	12
13	14	15	16	17	18	19
20	21	22	23	24	25	26
27	28	29	30	31		

SEPTEMBER

S	M	T	W	T	F	S
					1	2
3	4	5	6	7	8	9
10	11	12	13	14	15	16
17	18	19	20	21	22	23
24	25	26	27	28	29	30

OCTOBER

S	M	T	W	T	F	S
1	2	3	4	5	6	7
8	9	10	11	12	13	14
15	16	17	18	19	20	21
22	23	24	25	26	27	28
29	30	31				

NOVEMBER

S	M	T	W	T	F	S
			1	2	3	4
5	6	7	8	9	10	11
12	13	14	15	16	17	18
19	20	21	22	23	24	25
26	27	28	29	30		

DECEMBER

S	M	T	W	T	F	S
					1	2
3	4	5	6	7	8	9
10	11	12	13	14	15	16
17	18	19	20	21	22	23
24	25	26	27	28	29	30
31						

Work Around The Home

Remember *Check you have materials and tools needed*

Date

School Activities

Remember *Times, Location, Contact Name*

Date

Other

Remember

Date

Hobbies & Lessons

Remember *Materials, Practice, Studying*

Date

Health & Fitness

Remember *Dentist, Annual Check-Ups, Optometrist, Fitness Tests*

Date

Sports & Teams

Remember *Directions, Drivers, Coaches' Numbers, Times*

Date